CELLAR DOORS AND HOLLYHOCKS

Cellar Doors and Hollyhocks

An anthology of writing
by older Minnesotans
from the COMPAS Literary Post project

Edited by
Nancy Weber

Illustrated by
Rochelle Woldorsky

COMPAS, 1988

COMPAS
Literary Post
308 Landmark Center
75 West Fifth Street
Saint Paul, Minnesota 55102
Molly LaBerge, Executive Director
Margret Swanson, Program Director

Illustrations and cover design by Rochelle Woldorsky.

Cover drawing, "Minneapolis House Series" by Rochelle Woldorsky, courtesy of Holly Backus Eicher.

The title of this book is taken from an essay by Helen Foster.

COMPAS activities are made possible, in part, by grants from the Minnesota State Arts Board through an appropriation by the Minnesota Legislature; the National Endowment for the Arts; and a McKnight Foundation award administered by the Minnesota State Arts Board. COMPAS is a member agency of United Arts.

The COMPAS 1987 Literary Post program was supported by grants from the Blandin Foundation, Otto Bremer Foundation, Patrick and Aimee Butler Family Foundation, Medtronic Foundation, Ruth Mott Fund, Nash Foundation and the Witter Bynner Foundation for Poetry.

Special thanks to Annette Jung, Carol Bergeland, and Mary Becker for their indispensable help at COMPAS.

Table of Contents

CELLAR DOORS AND HOLLYHOCKS:
THE SOVEREIGNTY OF MEMORY

DRY BONES: CYCLES OF LOSS AND HEALING

COMPAS and Literary Post

COMPAS is the largest community arts agency in Minnesota, providing and sponsoring a variety of multi-disciplinary arts activities to people of all ages and abilities. Each year more than 170,000 Minnesotans participate in COMPAS programs. COMPAS demonstrates the many ways in which art can build a sense of community by bringing the arts into classrooms, nursing homes, churches, prisons, treatment centers, and neighborhoods.

Literary Post is a COMPAS creative writing program for older Minnesotans that is conducted through the mail. COMPAS mail order editors review the writing of Literary Post participants and they respond with critical suggestions, assignments and, most importantly, encouragement to continue writing.

Five hundred older Minnesotans participated in Literary Post this past year. Jonis Agee, Margot Kriel Galt, Mary Rockcastle, Bart Schneider and Nancy Weber served as the COMPAS mail order editors. Working from their homes, the editors helped senior writers shape and refine their memoirs, stories and poems.

Literary Post provided these five mail order editors with a unique glimpse into the lives of hundreds of older Minnesotans. Through their letters and manuscripts, the writers revealed very intimate, tragic and joyful moments from their lives — written with a clarity and honesty that comes after living six or more decades. *Cellar Doors and Hollyhocks* gives all of us a similar glimpse into their lives through this collection of stories and poems. This book is a tribute to those writers and to all older Minnesotans.

Margret Swanson
Program Director

Foreword

T he territories of memory are as diverse and breathtaking as those of the imagination. Often the boundary between the two is indistinguishable. And certainly there is little access to one without the other; for memory excites imagination, and imagination fills in outlines cast by the memory.

Each of the writers in this anthology travels the terrain of both. While some—Winnifred Mahle, Bart Hoglund, Betty Arhelger—recall childhood experience and use imagination to shape it for us, others—Lowell Haas, Doris Fuller Pylkas, Ebba Kingstrom—imagine themselves into the lives, even into the memories of others. Some of these writers relate directly, as Phyllis Peterson does, those moments when experience itself seems to cross beyond the borders of both memory and imagination.

Much of the work in this book is memoir, that combined story-essay form that seems, these days, to answer a deep hunger. It's the hunger of families for their own history, their separate identity; the hunger of individuals to tell "their story," and of listeners to hear them; the hunger that comes sometimes from events, even objects to get themselves written.

Different writers approach this memoir task differently. Lucile Arnold chose to write her memoirs in the form of letters to a granddaughter. Several writers record the life stories of others: Mary Berntson and Violet Backe tell their mothers' stories, Ken Kelly his father's. Still others set down for future generations stories from family oral tradition, as does Leah Haas with her tale "Rube Bartley and the Devil's Hound." Some take remembered experience and weave new fictions from it as Albert McClure does in "The Pro," while some simply tell it straight out and bold as Virginia Prestin does. Each of these writers has made thoughtful decisions about the relative roles imagination and memory are to play in their work—and about the form or shape in which to put the products of this combustible relationship.

There are, of course, also the poets. Poets worry less about distinctions like imagination vs. memory, fact vs. fiction than do prose writers. The experience of poetry, both writing and reading it, brings it all together in language as no other form can. Thus we get a wide range of poetic subjects and forms—all the way from the retelling of a story often heard in childhood, which Ethel Askov accomplishes in "Goldilocks and the Bares," to Meg Kramer's "Sonnet for March." Poems like Vernon Carlson's "Ode to Boots" and Helen Earle Simcox's "Orange" pay homage to otherwise ordinary, unnoticed things. Poems like "Fallen Leaves, Hidden Heart" by Roy Benjamin Moore spring sounds up off the page toward us. And those like "Bacon for Breakfast: Double Recipe" by Margaret Manship shake us into chuckling, another way of elevating the daily.

As you travel the pages of *Cellar Doors and Hollyhocks*, you will wander the borders of imagination and memory along with the writers of these stories, memoirs and poems. Your journey may not, however, end there, for this book invites you to ride into your own territories of memory and of imagination. Godspeed.

Nancy Weber
October, 1987

THE MARATHON: GROWING UP

The Marathon

Bart Hoglund
Walker, Minnesota

When I was a lad of six
it was my ordeal to run
across a windswept meadow
toward a forest of fir trees.
But it was the path to school
and a thing to be done
though the cost was cold feet
and other winter miseries.

I tried running backwards
to protect my face,
for the north wind was a sharp
and cold-hearted foe.
And at such times my feet
sought in vain to trace
that narrow packed trail
beneath the drifting snow.

But the forest was waiting
like a quiet warm room,
for its fir trees grew so close
that no breeze could intrude.
There the wind sighed overhead,
tossing tree tops as it fumed,
for it had no power
in that woodland's solitude.

A mile of that forest,
then another run,
plowing through the drifts
of a farmer's field.
Then a triumphant finish
when the race was won—
climbing the porch steps
as the last bell pealed.

Ripples and Ice
From the novel Early Light

Howard Hadley
Blaine, Minnesota

Q uite often our skating season was very short, or almost
nonexistent. A strong wind could cause the ice to freeze
in a rough, washboardy pattern, very unsatisfactory for skating.
Snow might fall heavily almost immediately after the ice was
safe to use. Although the various cousins and neighbor children
would solemnly agree to keep a specified area open as a rink,
I do not recall that any Aspen Bay rink ever lasted past the middle of December. The howling winds and heavy snowfalls,
sometimes combining like twin demons of chaos, would soon
put an end to the open surface so eagerly cleared by the first
group of volunteers. The boys who lived nearest to it would tire
of doing most of the work. Those who lived farther away would
come to it on Saturdays after the morning chores were done, op-
timistically carrying shovels and skates. Greeted by the stark,
white vision of five-foot snowdrifts on the formerly bare rink,
they would take a few half-hearted sweeps with their shovels
before concluding that some recreation came at too high a price.

Once every five years or so we would have a magnificient
skating season when the ice stayed safe and snow-free for two
or more weeks. Best of all was when a full moon lent its presence as well. You could skate south down the winding creek to
Ernie Linstrom's fence where the tangled trunks and branches
of our southern pasture brush looked black, beautiful, and mys-
terious in the moonlit winter night—or you could take the other
creek fork past Grandpa Hartman and Uncle Tom Long's homes
where there were more admirable combinations of light and
shadows to enjoy. But most satisfying of all, perhaps, was the
joyful glide north down the ever-widening bay. On the large ex-
panses of clear, smooth ice, we would pick up speed and then
leap over muskrat houses, or we would practice spinning, braking, and reversing direction. There was also just the delight of
seeing one's curving skate marks etched in the pristine ice.

When we heard the silvery ring of many skate blades and

4

other voices and laughter in the cold, clear air, we knew that we were drawing close to the large cove in front of Johnny Lund's house. Johnny, whose mother had drowned in the bay's black waters many years ago, was a cheerful, generous bachelor who welcomed the skaters to his house, as he did visitors at all times of the year. Our bodies were warmed by his fire as our hearts were warmed by his presence. Johnny was one of those rare individuals who not only loved people, but had an infectious wonder and pleasure in the commonplace events of everyday life.

On one of those resplendent nights my high school friend, John Hurt, and I skated down the creek shortly after supper when a great full moon was just rising behind the leafless poplars. We explored both creek branches and the main bay before playing tag, crack-the-whip, and hide-and-go-seek with the many neighboring young people and town friends who had journeyed to Aspen Bay so they might enjoy the fine sport at Johnny Lund's cove. We tiptoed up the bank on our skate blades, removed our skates at his kitchen door, and then stocking-footed it into the house which was crowded with guests who were resting tired ankles, drinking coffee, eating, and talking with Johnny and one another. Everything was good, but the talk was best. All night long we alternated between Johnny's house and the ice, from the moonlight to the crackling wood fire and the glow of the kerosene lamps. We skated home at about four a.m. so that we could crowd in an hour or two of sleep before morning cow milking time.

The bay widened again just past my Uncle Ed Hartman's place, who lived a quarter of a mile north of Johnny Lund. Uncle Ed's house sat on an inlet of the bay. The inlet's water was plenty deep for his boats and dock in the summer; it was too deep for a foolhardy youngster's escapade in the winter. One afternoon I was skating with my cousin Dave Hartman on the ice below his father's house. Dave, a year or two older than I, was an infinitely better skater and all-around athlete. The ice on the inlet was safe enough, except in one spot where the muskrats had been working. The water over the muskrat "hole," completely free of ice the day before, was now capped with a layer of very thin ice. When we got close to it, Dave glided gracefully by its edge on one skate, reaching out with the other to cut neatly away a piece of brittle crystal. My competitive reaction to this skillful ploy ("it doesn't cut any ice with me") was to glide slightly closer on a somewhat shaky blade, stretching my other skate as far as I dared to separate an even larger wafer of delicate ice from its mooring. The two of us continued this contest until I won. It was a Pyrrhic victory—after cutting off a satisfyingly large piece, I skated right into the hole.

At those glacial temperatures, the dark water seemed to sear my unwilling skin like flame. I did not subside into torpor by any means, but reached out frantically in all directions with spluttering desperation. Dave calmly learned over from the edge of the thicker ice and somehow, single-handedly, pulled me out without falling in himself. Once upon the ice, my overalls froze stiff, and a long strand of water weed refused to unstick when I unclenched my fist. While walking awkwardly on sodden skates from the now open muskrat hole, my ice-laden overalls literally clattered, and as I glanced over at Dave, the humor of the thing struck us both at once. We leaned into the winter wind and laughed on the way to the house. My laughter, coming through chattering teeth and blue lips, had a certain frigid, soprano tremor that did not subside until I rapidly changed to dry clothes while basking in great welcome waves of indoor heat.

Goldilocks and the Bares

Ethel Askov
Saint Louis Park, Minnesota

A little girl with long, golden curls
went for a walk in the woods.
Her name, as you might guess, was Goldilocks.
She walked and walked,
stopping at times to pick flowers,
to watch a squirrel climb a tree, or
to chase a butterfly.
At last she spied a little white house.
Goldilocks was tired.
She went to the door and knocked.
No one answered, so she opened the door
and walked in.
On the kitchen table were three bowls of soup:
a big bowl, a middle-sized bowl, and a tiny bowl.
Goldilocks was so hungry
she ate the soup from all three bowls.
She walked into the living room.
In front of the TV were three chairs:
a big chair, a middle-sized chair, and a tiny chair.
Goldilocks turned on the TV and sat down
on the tiny chair; the others looked too big.
The tiny chair broke. She got up and turned off the TV.
Seeing a staircase, she decided to explore further.
She climbed the stairs and saw three beds:
a big bed, a middle-sized bed, and a tiny bed.
By now Goldilocks had concluded
three people must live in this house:
a big person, a middle-sized person, and a tiny person.
Goldilocks was tired, so she crawled into the tiny bed
and fell fast asleep.
Before long she was wakened by loud voices.
She didn't know it yet, but Mr. Bare, Mrs. Bare
and Tiny Bare had come home.
They, too, had been for a walk in the woods.

The Bares were angry when they saw
their soup gone and the tiny chair broken.
"Who did this?" Mr. Bare shouted.
"Who broke my chair?" screamed Tiny Bare.
"Let's look upstairs," whispered Mrs. Bare.

Goldilocks heard them climbing the stairs.
She was frightened; she pretended to sleep.
Just as the Bares reached the top step
Goldilocks opened her eyes
and gasped in astonishment.
Never before had she seen grown-ups
without clothes.
Goldilocks sprang out of bed, rushed
to the open window, jumped to the ground below,
and ran all the way home.

Inspired by the reading of Anne Sexton's "Cinderella."

A Ride on the Train

Winnifred Myers Mahle
Wabasha, Minnesota

Peggy decided to carry the small teddy bear. She might need his furry comfort during the new experience. Mama had carefully packed China-headed Gwendolyn and Boy Doll among the clothes.

It was more than a mile from home to the train depot, and the summer sun was hot. Papa set the suitcases on the station platform, pushed the derby to the back of his head, and wiped the perspiration from his face and forehead.

Peggy and White Teddy sought the safety of Mama's black serge skirt when a shrill whistle announced the coming of the iron monster. Peggy peeked out cautiously. A thin trail of smoke lost itself in the blue above. The train sounds went from "Choo-choo-choo" to CHoo-CHoo-CHoo" and then to "CHOOA- CHOOA-CHOOA" as the great bars connecting the spoked wheels moved forward and backward, slower and slower, then stopped. There was a clash of metal as each car bumped the one in front of it. "SSHHHish." A jet of steam came from the locomotive's underside. She had been excited about the trip to see Grandpa and Grandma Goltz and her dozen cousins who lived in the same area, but all this commotion gave her goose bumps.

The door of the coach opened; the conductor climbed down the steps, placed a stool on the ground, and helped the passengers descend to the brick platform.

Mama and Papa stood with the line of people who had come out of the low, dingy, red-brick depot. The sign at the end of the building spelled WORTHINGTON. Papa had bought two tickets to Balaton which was far away—sixty miles. And they must change trains.

Papa handed the two heavy suitcases to the conductor, kissed Peggy and Mama, then waited to wave and throw a kiss.

"Up we go." The conductor smiled as he swooshed Peggy onto the coach. In her left arm Mama carried a white shoe box tied with string. Her large, black Sunday purse hung from her elbow. With the right hand she daintily raised her long skirt so that she wouldn't trip as she went up the steps.

One suitcase was in the baggage rack above the window; the other sat at Mama's feet. Peggy heard the conductor call, "All aboard." With a slight lurch and "CHuug-CHuug-CHuug," the train moved forward.

Peggy's feet and half the length of her skinny legs stuck straight out from the plump, prickly, red-plush seat. She leaned against the high, straight, back and admired her shiny-black patent leather shoes with white kid tops. Wind from the open window blew her hair. "Oh!" she exclaimed, jerking forward and putting her hand over one eye.

"A cinder," Mama said, "from the engine. Blink. Sometimes tears will wash it away." But they didn't. Mama twisted a corner of her hanky to make it firm. Peggy tipped her head back while Mama used her thumb to pull down Peggy's lower lid and her pointed finger to push up Peggy's upper lid. The cinder was in the corner. Mama removed it with her hanky, then held the rascal where Peggy could see it. When she sniffed and smiled, Mama gave her the hanky to blow her nose.

"I'm thirsty." Mama reached to the very bottom of her purse and drew out a small rim of bright metal. Peggy grasped the bottom with one hand, the top with the other, and pulled. There it was—a collapsible drinking cup. Peggy slid off the seat and walked to the end of the car where a round tank stood. Standing on tiptoe to turn the small brass faucet, she held her cup under the slow trickle of water

"Not too full," Mama warned.

Peggy walked slowly back to her seat, steadying herself on those she passed. Once, on a particularly rough piece of track, the car swayed. Water splashed from the cup onto her black sateen dress trimmed with pink. Would it leave a spot, Peggy wondered?

She stood with her back leaning against the edge of the seat, slowly sipped, and watched the telephone poles chase each other past the window. The wheels of the coach sang, "Cluckity-luckity-luckity-luckity." Turning the cup upside down, she patted its bottom to make sure every drop was out, pushed it to its narrow rim size, and handed it to Mama.

10

With her finger, Peggy traced the letters on the door at the end of the car, sounding them as her teacher had taught. "La—dies," she said aloud. Peggy patted Mama's knee and looked at her shyly. Mama went with her because the spring on the door was too strong for a little girl. In the small room, the train noises were louder—"Rackity-rackity-bumpity-bumpity." When Peggy lifted the toilet lid, the tune changed to "Clankety-clankety-blampity-blampity." The shining track lay on crosswise wooden ties making a runaway ladder.

"Ooh!" Peggy exclaimed. "It makes me dizzy!"

Mama stood close. Peggy put both arms tightly around Mama's legs. Later she washed her hands in a small brass sink with a brass push-down handle on the faucet. Later the conductor locked the toilet, Mama explained, "He does that when the train is several miles from a town, then unlocks it again several miles on the other side."

When the train whistle sounded a long, shrill blast, Peggy leaned toward the window because that was the signal before the train came to a road. She might see a horse and buggy waiting to cross the track. Sometimes the horse jumped and shied, frightened. Farm wagons with loads of hay were common. Occasionally was there an automobile. At one station, a train going the opposite direction stood on another track.

"What is that big striped thing on the front of the engine that looks like a piece of pie?"

"That's called a cow-catcher. There's one on our train, too. You were probably too busy being scared to notice when the engine went by."

"Does it really catch cows?"

"If they happen to be on the track, it shoves them off. I suppose the cow-catcher would pick up anything, preventing a possible wreck."

Peggy looked across the aisle where a young woman and a very small boy were unwrapping a package. "Mama, is it time for supper?"

At the end of the dainty gold chain around her neck, a gold watch was tucked into Mama's skirt band. She clicked the cover open with her thumb and smiled. "Yes. It's almost six o'clock."

Mama untied the string from the shoe box and took off the

cover. Peggy carefully unfolded the wax paper saved from the corn flakes box. "Goody!" she exclaimed, "Woodstocks!" Peggy had named Mama's special sandwiches after a small town they'd visited in Papa's old Studebaker. Mama mashed hard-boiled eggs with a fork, added her own salad dressing, salt, pepper, then vinegar and mustard to give the filling some zing. "My very most favorite," Peggy said as she took a big bite. Under the sandwiches, Peggy found fat sugar cookies for dessert.

Later, Mama and Peggy watched the summer sun float across the prairie, painting the whole sky rose and gold as it went to rest behind the hills near Mankato. Soon after, the brakeman came by with a long, lighted rod. Starting at one end of the car, he tilted each globe on the ceiling above the aisle, turned a jet to let the gas come through, and touched the glowing rod to the lamp. There was a gentle "pouf," a flame, and the globe was replaced. Peggy watched, fascinated. "Like magic," she said.

Another train man came through the car carrying a large basket of fruit—smooth, ripe bananas, shiny red apples, and the largest oranges Peggy had ever seen. All looked delicious, but Peggy did not ask for any. She knew they would cost too much. Imagine her surprise when Mama stopped the man and told Peggy she might choose one. The banana was tempting, but what would she do with its jacket? The orange might be mostly skin, and peeling it would be messy. She picked out the apple with the rosiest cheek. Peggy patted Mama's hand for a "thank you," and offered her a bite. Mama smiled and shook her head. Peggy smiled back, remembering that when Mama ate an apple at home she cut it into slices because her false teeth couldn't bite into it.

"How many towns before Balaton?"

"I don't know, but it will be after midnight when we get there."

In the dim light Peggy noticed several children curled up on the seats, their heads in their mothers' laps. Some grown-ups slept with their heads thrown back, others with chins on chests. One man snored loudly. No one was talking. Peggy curled her legs on the seat, leaned against her mother's arm, and sank her teeth into the juicy fruit.

She must have fallen asleep because the next thing she knew,

12

Mama was putting Peggy's arms in her coat sleeves and saying, "Here are your purse and Teddy to carry."

"My apple! Where's my apple?"

"In my purse." Mama had rescued the half-eaten fruit when Peggy dosed off.

"Are we at Grandpa's?"

"No, we are in Mankato. We must change to another train which will take us to Balaton."

They waited only a short time in the depot, and were soon on the last leg of their journey. Peggy finished eating her apple, curled her legs up on the seat and put her head in Mama's lap. Both slept.

They wakened when the conductor entered the car and called, "Next stop, Balaton," as he collected the ticket stubs.

Uncle George met them at the depot and carried the suitcases. During the five-block walk to Grandpa's house, Mama and Uncle George asked about each other's families. He wasn't much of a talker, but his smile was friendly. He and Aunt Gertrude lived with Grandpa and Grandma since Grandma was too crippled with rheumatism to keep house. She walked slowly with the help of a cane. Almost all day she knit long, narrow strips of cloth into rugs which she planned to give to the grandchildren.

Grandma got out of bed to greet her oldest child, Peggy's mama. She wore a white nightie with a ruffle at the neck, a flowered robe, and a white nightcap that tied under her chin. Peggy's mama kissed Grandma and said something Peggy couldn't understand. Then Grandma held her arms out to Peggy who felt a little bashful and Grandma kissed her and said something which sounded like "vee gates." Peggy said, "Hello, Grandma."

Grandpa and Grandma had come from Germany when Mama was nine years old. They had never learned English, and Peggy couldn't speak German except for some name-calling words like "mad cat" and "dumb donkey" taught to her by her German speaking cousins. So for the rest of the visit Grandma and Peggy mostly exchanged smiles, the same in any language.

The next day, Peggy made the trip on the train sound so exciting that all the cousins hoped they might someday have a ride in a coach pulled by a huffing, puffing locomotive.

13

Red is Rare

Alice Holcher
Hopkins, Minnesota

As I color Santa's clothes and nose
    How fast red goes;
I've no scarlet left for a cherry tart
    Or a Valentine heart.
Could Chuck Cardinal stand to be seen
    In a shade of green?
Impatiens and roses prefer a red hue.
    Geraniums too.
Old Glory won't look like itself
    If crayoned in delft.
Whoever heard of a rocket's *tan* glare
    When bursting in air?
The little red schoolhouse says with a frown,
    "Don't draw me brown."
The silo and barn cry every day
    When I color them gray.
Mr. Crayola, can't you instead
    Put in my crayon box much more red?

Promises

Mary Berntson
Minneapolis, Minnesota

W henever my mother, Clarice, heard me make a casual bargain with a child, she would remind me about Lars. Lars was a coarse, scruffy old man who used to come to the parsonage frequently to visit with her father, the preacher. My mother told me that whenever she saw Lars' buggy drive into their road, she would scoot for the house, hoping that he would not see her before her short toddler's legs could carry her up the steep narrow staircase to the safety of her corner of the bedroom. Lars and his wife had lost their four-year-old daughter to lung fever many years before. His heart still ached from the loss, however, and whenever he saw a little girl he tried to assuage that ache by holding her on his lap.

In spite of being the third child in the always busy parsonage, Clarice was an unusually shy little girl. Her usual place when most visitors came to call was behind her mother, clinging to Mama's leg as firmly as ivy clung to the church walls. When prompted to say hello to the visitor, she would peek around the edge of Mama's apron with her round blue eyes carefully veiled beneath their lids and whisper "Gud dag." Even before the words were uttered, she would retreat to her haven behind Mama.

Whenever Lars did see Clarice, he would try to coax her to climb up on his lap. One day he came before she had time to escape up the stairs, and she stood quaking behind Mama's sturdy frame. "Come in, Lars," Mama welcomed him. "Reverend Denvold should be here any minute now. Here, sit down." Mama almost fell over the little girl as they moved away from the door, but Lars acted oblivious to the fact that Clarice was even in the room. He took a small, clay penny doll from his cavernous pocket. He held it in his huge hand, turning it this way and that, as if examining it for possible flaws. He showed it to Mama and asked if she had ever seen another doll as beautiful as this. "I saw it in the case at Gus' store on my way over here today. It reminded me of my little Kara. So I bought it. But now

15

I'm afraid if I bring it home, my wife will start to cry. I don't know what possessed me to buy it. I wonder if you might know of someone I could give it to?"

Clarice's curiosity overcame her timidity. She twisted around the edge of Mama's leg just far enough so she could see Lars. He turned away slightly and held the doll up close to the window. Clarice edged further away from Mama's protection. One tentative step, and then another. But she still couldn't really see the doll, hidden as it was in Lars' hand. And oh, how she had been wanting one of those penny dolls. Her foot was midair on her third step away from Mama when Lars turned in apparent surprise to see her. "Well, hello there little Clarice. How are you today?" He absent-mindedly turned the doll between his gnarled thumb and forefinger. "I was just showing your mama this little dolly. I wonder if you know anyone who would like to have it."

Clarice darted back to the safety of Mama's calico skirt like a startled gopher. Lars continued his conversation with Mama, seemingly unaware of the little face peeking out at him. "You know, Missus, if I knew some little girl who would sit on my lap for a little while I would give her this doll. I don't suppose Clarice would want to do that?

"Come now, Clarice. Come out and see Lars. He won't bite," Mama coaxed. "Don't you want to . . . Oh, for land's sake, what is your brother Herman hollering about now? I better go check. You stay here with Lars now. I'll be right back. No, don't come tagging after me." Mama tugged the little arms from around her leg and ran out the kitchen door to see what Herman wanted. Clarice stood stone still. She was all alone with Lars.

"Come here, Clarice. Come sit on my lap. I haven't held a little girl in my lap for a long time now. Come sit here while we wait for your mama," he pleaded. "She said your papa was on his way back from the church, and I want to talk to him. Come sit with me while I wait."

Clarice stood motionless. Her blue eyes widened. Tears trembled on the brims, threatening to tumble over the edge. She liked to sit on Papa's lap, but she didn't want to sit on Lars' lap.

"If you come sit on my lap I will give you this dolly. Come,

16

sit." he patted his knee. "Come. Wouldn't you like to have this dolly?"

Clarice looked at Lars. He continued to pat his knee with one giant hand. The tiny penny doll was dwarfed in his other. She was sorely tempted. Why didn't Mama come back? Where was Papa? Why did Lars have to bring that doll here anyway? Why didn't he just go home and take the doll with him? Maybe she could just hold the doll for a minute. Maybe.

She took a tentative step closer to this big bear of a man who smelled of horses. She stopped. The huge hand continued thumping on his coarse wool trouser. If only she could see the doll better.

"Did you ever see a nicer doll than this?" he coaxed. He held the doll right out in front of her. She reached to touch it, but he drew his hand back. Involuntarily her little legs carried her forward. As she reached for the doll, hairy arms lifted her up. She was sitting on Lars' lap! She sat there gingerly, waiting for him to hand her the doll.

Just then Papa came into the kitchen. Lars stood up to greet him, and the little girl slid down his scratchy woolen-trousered legs to the floor. She looked up and waited expectantly for Lars to give her the doll. He didn't even see her. He was busy talking to Papa and waving both hands as he talked. The doll had disappeared into his pocket.

Within minutes, the two men were on their way out the door, leaving the little girl standing there stunned. He had said he would give her the doll if she would sit on his lap. Even though he had tricked her into it, she did sit on his lap. But he hadn't given her the doll. He had broken his promise. Mama and Papa were always telling Clarice and her brothers that they must never break a promise.

My mother never forgot the man who had broken his promise to her, and she always admonished me, "Never promise a child a reward or a punishment unless you mean it. I suppose I never really forgave that man for not giving me that doll, although I'm sure he probably bought it just for me, and really intended to give it to me. He just forgot. But he violated a child's trust by forgetting, and I never forgot that feeling of betrayal."

The Scar

Betty Arhelger
Minneapolis, Minnesota

W hen we moved to Mayborn I was four years old and my scar was barely three. Plunging from my shoulder to the knuckles of my left hand and wrapping around to my elbow, scarlet and ridged as the waves of an angry ocean, it was easily the most outstanding thing about me.

I was exceedingly proud of this scar and displayed it as often as possible. It never failed to elicit little gasps and moans of pity. Almost every adult queried my parents about it in my presence. I enjoyed the attention. Most children, on the other hand, rarely bothered with more than the most cursory questions. Except for Leona.

Leona was five, and she and her mother were coming to call on the new neighbors. Sitting on the cedar chest in front of the large bay window of a house with its furnishings not yet settled, I could see Leona and Mrs. Jasperson making their way across the vacant lot that separated our houses. Mrs. Jasperson carried a dish wrapped in red and white checked cloth and picked her steps carefully among the patches of ice still left in early March. Leona carried on an animated conversation which continued until they reached our door and right through the initial introductions when she got her first glimpse of my arm. As if not to be outdone in a color contest, her face turned bright red. She opened her mouth wide, took one deep breath and shrieked. None of Mrs. Jasperson's angry, embarrassed admonitions could muffle Leona's screams. Not even the hasty offer of frosted cupcakes could soothe her frightened sobs.

I was enchanted. Here, indeed, was a power of a heady sort. Apologies extended and accepted, the adults sat down to the retelling of the old story. The story I never tired of. I preened a bit and crept closer.

"She was barely fourteen months old," my mother said. "She was so tiny and really a very good baby. She never got into things—I suppose that's what made it so hard. At any rate, I was doing the washing and she was sitting in the big kitchen rocking chair, rocking her doll. I could *hear* the rocker creaking and hear her singing, so I knew she was all right. Well, I had a kettle of water on the stove for starch, you know, and it was boiling furiously. The first thing I knew I heard the rocker tip and heard her scream. The rocker had traveled across the linoleum and bumped against the stove. One of the spindles had hooked the handle of the kettle, upsetting it on Betty. What saved her, of course, from extensive burns was the fact that the rocker tipped, covering her head and back. She flung out her arm, and that got burned. She had on a hand knit sweater, really quite heavy, that held in the steam and caused such a terrible burn."

Mrs. Jasperson touched her eyes and lips with her handkerchief, and I sighed with satisfaction. In the corner, Leona, hiccuping over a cup of hot chocolate, had lost interest in the entire affair.

By the time I reached school age several things had happened. As I'd grown, so had my arm. In fact, I had begun to grow out of my scar. It had receded from my knuckles back across my hand until it extended from my sleeve only an inch or so. A small space appeared between my shoulder and lower arm. Also, I had learned to exploit the scar to avoid work and extract pity.

If my parents were aware of this they ignored it, probably for reasons of guilt and an almost superstitious relief that the scalding water had not hit my face. I had often heard expressions of this relief and had erroneously concluded that I was beautiful.

But my greatest pride, and the reason for my considerable popularity, was the pit in the scar on the top front of my arm. When the keloid tissues were building up, a sworl of slightly raised scar had left a pit in the center of it. It was about a quarter of an inch deep, and I could "plant" it with a violet, a clover, or even a sprig of parsley. Until a boy with a removable glass eye moved to town, I had held front and center stage.

My parents didn't seem to see the beauty of my scar, and over the years we consulted various specialists about its removal. The last consultant we saw told them that the only way to graft this burn was to break my arm and affix it to the skin of my back for a period of two years, then cut it free and reset the arm. My mother grew faint at the telling and had to be conducted to a window for fresh air. The doctor also suggested that with the coming of puberty the scar would be greatly absorbed.

Among the many pleasures and privileges the scar afforded me over the years, certainly the greatest was explaining it to questioners when my parents weren't around. A ride on the streetcar, if I were visiting my grandmother in the Cities, or a trip to the library, was certain to turn up at least one curious woman who would bend low and murmur solitiously, "You poor dear. How did you ever get that dreadful scar?" I prided myself that although I could feel the question coming, I never prepared answers in advance. I simply let it gush to the surface.

Perhaps it would be, "Well, it was during the awful forest fire when all the woods were doomed. I plunged in and put it out single-handedly. I have a medal at home from President Roosevelt, but my mother won't let me wear it everyday." Or perhaps, more somberly, "Our house was burning down and *someone* had to save the twins. I dashed in and picked up Priscilla and then went back for Prunella, but I was too late. I stirred about in the fire with my left arm, you know, but I never found her."

When my mother finally became aware of my antics, it was too late. I was addicted to the stories and I discovered that my father wasn't really angry about it. I had overhead a conversation: "Listen, Ruth, if they've got the gall to ask her, they can damn well listen to her answers." So I continued my stories, saving the nicest ones for sales clerks who offered to find me a proper dress as they crooned, "Something with long sleves, of course."

Adolescence proved the doctor no liar. As the years passed, so did some of the angry red of my scar. The ridges flattened somewhat, and the smoother surface became increasingly more beige and white. The pit alone remained to remind me of former glory, but eventually this too went the way of modern science. One afternoon, a few weeks after a lovely girl at a dinner party had asked the hostess to be seated away from me because the scar made her feel ill, my husband, a young surgeon, invited me into his operating room and removed the pit.

No more can I plant a petite flower. People seldom stare at me now, and it has been years since I have been asked how I got the scar. Too bad, really, because I have this wonderful story. "My husband was smoking in bed, you know and . . . "

20

A Shift of Power

Virginia Prestin
Brooklyn Park, Minnesota

As we listened to the radio, laughing, we leaned back in our chairs and propped our feet on the registers, so hot air flowed up our skirts. It was cozy, comfortable and fun. Mom was sitting in the rocker next to the mending basket in the dining room. A ten-foot arch divided this from the living room forming a huge room about twenty-five feet long. All the rooms were large, probably a reaction to ten years of living in that first tiny, temporary, four-room house. Sis and I shared the register around the corner in the living room. Our long day was ending. We were still in our chore clothes of faded cotton dresses, lisle stockings, warm but frayed woolen sweaters.

Sis and I usually pulled a brother's bib-top overall over our own clothes for chores, but Mom was too heavy for that, so she wore long underwear under her stockings. Every garment we wore was faded, frayed and mended, but in that time and place this didn't necessarily indicate poverty, only frugality and good money management. Further evidence of non-poverty was the lovely new radio, a floor-model Zenith in a dark wooden cabinet with rounded corners. It was the very latest in streamlined design, and was the only new piece of furniture in the room. The radio had a battery, and keeping it charged was a constant concern.

The program ended. Seventy-nine Wistful Vista disappeared, and the funny fantasy world of Fibber McGee and Molly was gone for another week. I wondered what program would come next. Perhaps it was concern for the battery that made Mom reach out and turn the radio off, but she didn't mention that. Instead, she said abruptly, "You girls go to bed now."

I was stunned. It was too sudden! The sophisticated world of radioland disappeared like a fadeout in a movie. In its place the big dining room faded in. The round oak table appeared, covered by a worn oilcloth, then the straight oak chairs, the varnished maple floor and the gray-patterned linoleum with paths worn to the kitchen and hallway. At the south and west windows were matching white Priscilla curtains, starched and ironed. I remembered ironing them myself, taking care with each ruffle, making many trips with the heavy sadirons, from kitchen cookstove to the ironing board in the dining room. The ironing board was homemade and had no legs; it was laid across the backs of two chairs for ironing. The curtains were Montgomery Ward's cheapest and so scanty they barely covered the double west window. But they looked fresh and made a pretty framework for two brave red geraniums. The plants grew in tin cans with shreds of removed labels still making white lines up the sides of the cans. We never bought canned food, (we considered that a sign of shiftlessness), but our neighbors sometimes did and these bean cans were from them. The ornate treadle sewing machine made a perfect plant stand.

The yellow flame of the lamp cast a circle of light on the faded top section of oilcloth on the table. The edges were unfaded; they hung down in shadow, but I knew the blue and green flower print so well that it seemed to me the lamplight reached even there. The lamp perfumed the room with a faint, pleasant smell of kerosin. This mingled with the leftover aroma of homemade chili from our supper. Mom was serious about her cooking; you would think we had delicate appetites which had to be coaxed, rather than the robust ones we actually had. The chili had been seasoned just right, and it was rich with beans and beef and home-canned tomatoes. We'd eaten it with great slabs of homemade bread, fresh butter, and large glasses of our fresh milk. Dessert had been home-canned peaches with slices of fresh, homemade coffee cake. No one would be hungry again until breakfast time.

I decided to make a protest. This was in keeping—we never switched roles in our domestic drama. Sis was fourteen, the older, sensible, obedient daughter, always stable and to be depended on. I was twelve, the former baby of the family, unstable, disobedient, always ready to challenge authority. This time I had a faint hope that Sis might be an ally; I was sure she wanted another program as much as I did. But one glance at her ended that hope. Her face was as placid and passive as always and I was on my own.

"We want to find out what comes next," I said, in a reasonable tone of voice.

Mom's voice was slightly irritated as she said, "You don't need to find out. You get to bed. We have to get up early in the morning."

It was true that five o'clock was early, but I said, "It's only eight clock! We always get up in time for chores." That was true also.

"That's because you go to bed on time. Get to bed right now!"

Now I heard the beginning of the grim, implacable tone in Mom's voice which had been directed at me as long as I could remember. From my earliest memories I heard it saying, "That's good enough for *her!*" "She can just wait until last." "Will you stop being such a cry-baby? That bath water is *not* hot." "Oh, why do you have to cry every time I comb your hair? If you didn't run around so wild it wouldn't be so snarled. Sis never cries when I comb her hair, but you have to be a cry-baby!" On and on it went, a never ending litany of fault finding, criticism and rough handling which including her looking the other way when my older brothers teased and tormented me when the mood struck them. Pop was out of the house most of the time, working outdoors, and it would take thirty years before I would understand that his presence had been the only protection I had. But Pop had died the previous July, and I still didn't have an answer to the riddle of Mom's abuse. This particular evening there was something new – she was including Sis, treating us as one unit, "you girls."

In spite of growing uneasiness I risked one more protest.

"The boys aren't even home yet. How come we have to get to bed and they don't?

"The boys" were my three older brother. They were off for the evening doing whatever it was that teenage boys did with friends. My two little brothers, known as "the kids," were already asleep.

"The boys are older than you. And don't give me any more of your lip – you get to bed right now!"

Talking back to parents was a heinous sin for youngsters, and only very lax and weak parents permitted it. My parents were never lax or weak. Talking back was a cause of gossip among neighbors. It ruined a child's reputation fast. I didn't have nerve enough to risk such a soiled reputation with my peers or with adults, and I knew we would go to bed – now. No more discussion, period. But I wasn't liking it, and a slow burn of anger flickered in my stomach as we walked to the hallway to wash up.

The washstand and slop bucket stood in the hallway where, in the future, a sink could be installed. Death caught up to Pop before he could finish all his plans, and we were getting along now just as we had in the tiny, temporary, four-room house which had sheltered us for ten years while he'd built this one. We washed in a basin, emptied it into the slop bucket, carried it outdoors and poured the contents on top of the ground and let nature dispose of the waste. A tiny closet off the hallway was planned for a future toilet, and we kept a communal pot there to save dressing up and running out to the privy when it wasn't convenient, or when we felt lazy. Next day that was emptied into the privy, and again nature took care of it.

Sis and I took turns with the wash basin, with brushing teeth, and with the pot in the closet. We didn't speak, not even arguing whose turn it was and who was taking too long. Mom was silent, rocking, as we passed her and hurried through the shadowy living room to the stairway. The clock ticked as usual on the shelf above the radio. As we opened the door to the stairway it squeaked on the hinges, as always – a normal, comforting sound in this angry silence.

There was no light on the stairs. We didn't need one – we knew every inch of the twelve, varnished oak steps. As we ran up, they were as solid under our feet as when Pop had nailed them into place, three years earlier. The air was frosty and fresh smelling. There was solid, varnished oak floor in the hallway and in our room – everything stable and normal. Why did it seem that things were shifting in my world?

Hanging a door on our room was one of the things Pop hadn't got done. In place of the missing door Mom had nailed up an old green drapery panel of a heavy but threadbare material. This piece of fabric was around the house all my life – sometimes it was a door, as now, sometimes a blanket, sometimes a throw for a living room cot, sometimes a tablecloth for a picnic. It was faded and thin, a matching fringe at the bottom was almost totally disintegrated. This curtain kept heat in our bedroom while the hallway stayed chilly all winter.

The curtain dropped shut behind us. In the dark room the west and south windows glowed from the moonlight outdoors. Snowy fields gleamed for half a mile, then the dark woods began, and I knew how it was out there—serene and lovely. Jack rabbits playing in open patches of moonlight, owls slipping through the branches, mice diving into their tunnels just in time—or not in time—and then a furry little squeak as the owl took off again. I wished myself out there with them, sliding my skis along the path to Reynolds' house, watching the rippling ribbons of shadows on snowbanks. Life and death were lovely and terrible out there. Life and death were lovely and terrible indoors, too, and I felt torn between indoors and outdoors.

Sis lit the lamp and the glowing windows turned to mirrors, great black rectangles on the white plastered walls. Sis undressed silently, but I grumbled to her in an undertone, "Who does she think she is? We're not little kids anymore; why should we have to go to bed at eight o'clock?"

Sis didn't answer. Who could know what her thoughts were? Sometimes I suspected that she didn't have any thoughts.

She was in her pajamas and climbing into her side of the bed while I sat on my side, still dressed. My anger was feeding on itself, and I felt as though it was rising toward the ceiling like a visible cloud of steam, while more pressure built up inside me.

As I sat there, a hornet bussed in my left ear: "Run away! Run away!" A second hornet buzzed in my right ear: "Where would you run to?" First hornet: "Aunt Etta has always been kind. She would take you in." Second hornet: "She's in Chicago, and that's three hundred miles away! How would you get there?" First hornet: "You could hitchhike." Second hornet: "Remember Ruth Kresge!"

Indeed I remembered Ruth Kresege. She and her friend ran away once. They hitchhiked, but the police picked them up before they reached Milwaukee, and they were brought home in disgrace. That would be more humiliating than being sent to bed at eight o'clock like a six-year-old kid. I shook my head and the hornets were gone.

I started to undress and sat with a shoe in my hand, thinking, I'd like to throw it at her! Then I remembered that she was still in the dining room, right below us. A lifetime of farm work and softball games had developed good muscles in my arms, and I could pitch ball as well as my older brother could. I wound up for a pitch, but overhand, not underhand as for softball. The shoe hit the floor with a satisfying jolt, bounced once and lay on its side under the dresser.

There wasn't a sound downstairs.

I listened to the silence. Soon I took off the other shoe, wound up again, and threw the best pitch of my life. It was louder than the first one.

Now I heard a sound. She was heavy but not flabby, her body as solid with muscles as my own from the same kind of physical work. I heard her lift that heavy body from the rocker; then her footsteps moved slowly to the downstairs hallway, her worn-down slippers shuffling a little. Why the hallway? Why didn't she come directly to the stairs?

Next her solid footsteps returned to the dining room, passed through the living room, and again the door to the stairs squeaked as she opened it. I counted the steps as she climbed, my defiance mounting with each step. She had always been a massive, powerful figure to me, but now I felt equal to her. With adrenalin pumping in my body, I felt strong and ready to fight, and I wasn't afraid. I would welcome a fight.

She reached our room and pushed the heavy curtain aside. As it dropped behind her, I saw why she'd made that detour to the downstairs hallway. Pop's razor strap was still kept on a nail there, and now it drooped from her right hand. This was the instrument of discipline for all seven of us as we grew up. I couldn't remember how it felt, it had been that long since it was used on me.

She stared at me, and I stared back. Her face had a new expression—on anyone else I would interpret that look as fear, but since she was fearless, it couldn't be that. Sis lay rigid in the bed, not making a sound.

I noticed something else that was new. Even though I was sitting and she was standing, her eyes were not much above the level of mine. Our blue eyes locked, and I fleetingly remembered my wish for someone in the family to have brown eyes. I was bored with blue.

Long moments went by. We were three frozen people, unmoving, as though we had been there forever.

At last she said, "You get right in that bed and get to sleep now!"

I stared, astonished, as she turned and lifted the curtain. Her stocky figure in the faded print dress, the frayed gray sweater, disappeared.

That powerful, unsolved riddle moved to the stairs. As I listened to the heavy, slow footsteps going down, down and down, I knew that her power was draining away with each step.

Then as she reached the stairway door and it squeaked shut behind her, I felt something new and strange. I felt the first, faint stirring of sympathy for my mother.

BACON FOR BREAKFAST: DAILINESS

Bacon for Breakfast: Double Recipe

Margaret M. Manship
Mahtomedi, Minnesota

First you have to get a man
To bring home the bacon.

All right, let's assume
You've got the bacon
And the man
Now to get a pan.

Not cast iron
That breaks if you
Drop it on the floor.

Don't use teflon coating,
It's a nuisance.
The fire has to be just so
And the utensils, too.

The best thing is
Old fashioned steel.
Look in Grandma's attic
And while you're there
Don't ask her about frying bacon.
In her day
Even a five-year-old
Knew how to fry bacon.
    (Oh, she's rafting down
    the Colorado River!)
Well, do you have the
Key to her house?

Let's see, man, bacon, pan.
So we'll get started.
Go slow—allow enough time.
It may take you 15 minutes

30

To get the strips apart.
Now, lay them in the pan
Turn on the heat
Not too high.

Hey, wait a minute
Don't go away!
Can't take time out for
answering the phone
Or getting Jim
Out of bed.
Did you look at the clock
Feed the cat
Or set the table?
So—it's your own fault!

Bacon won't stand for
Inattention.

Turn on the fan
Shut off the smoke alarm
    (Well, why did he put
    it up so high?)
Snarl at him
Kick the cat.
Separate some more strips
Start over.

Turn the bacon when it's
Done on one side
    (There's no way to tell
    this for sure.)

OK—it looks almost
Done on the second side.
Ah, you should have removed
It from the pan
Two minutes ago
But it will have to do.

Pick the least
Scorched pieces for him.
Give yours to the cat.
    (He's pretty persnickety
    isn't he?)

Try again tommorrow.

Or would you
Rather have oatmeal?

an excerpt from
Spencer

Anna Nickol
Minneapolis, Minnesota

"Gold fever is the most malignant and potentially the most crippling disease known to man."

The pundit wheeled his portable desk within a circle of light cast by a wide-shaded gasoline lamp which hung above a poker table. Poker was a gamble Benjamin Harrison Dormer understood and practiced. His usual players were waiting for him to prepare his preliminary report to the stage company so the game could get going. The stage was later than usual, and no news had come in. It was a winter night in Spencer, one of the last along the crooked trail of gold camps that followed Sutter's Mill after 1849. It owed little of its continuance to climate, and both stage and freight wagons had slowed as snow settled deep between the hills.

The town had stalled at a population which barely exceeded fifteen hundred human bodies. Whether these bodies contained souls was still an unresolved question in the pessimistic mind of Benjamin Harrison Dormer. But when he explained their foibles by identifying them as disease, he was better able to accept them.

Ben had an Oliver typewriter with which he picked out his reports. The task did not waste a great amount of his time, but the company knew they had a good man, and they made him as comfortable as possible. This comfort had its negative side. At times the station house was filled to the doors with men whose own quarters were far less comfortable. In general, Ben reaped a certain compensation for having put up with them and their muddy footprints, not to mention their loud and contentious voices, by relieving them of coin, greenbacks and small quantities of "dust." The strike at Spencer was not a spectacularly manificent one, but Ben hoped that when the town died in its tracks, he would have a nest egg to tide him over from one job to the next. Soldiering had not paid off well in the late, unmourned Spanish-American conflict.

In a corner closest to the flat-topped, potbellied stove hunched a tall, fearfully thin Englishman, the real article, only a few years out of that tight little, right little isle. He had tacked a newspaper to the wall behind him, but drafts came through and around it. He longed for the poker game, which would help him forget his discomfort. But when no one answered Ben's challenge to gold seekers, the Englishman commented mildly:

"Is it really a disease, Ben, or just an aberration?"

"So far," put in a third, "none of us is so crippled he couldn't drag himself in here to get warm."

Ben grinned. He knew that Boniface, red-faced, mutton-chop-whiskered owner and operator of The Spencer House, the town's new and only hotel, didn't need to come to the stage station for warmth, and it was doubtful the non-paying guests at the station were much noisier than Boniface's own four kids — or much less.

"Most of us tonight don't owe our daily bread to yellow dust or mucking in the creek, though. The entire population probably found the trip over here even colder than staying home," spoke another, the youngest of the present group.

All of them had come in the hope of winning at poker. All, that is, except this skinny, bucktoothed seventeen-year-old, know to all as Bun. He owed his name to his buck teeth. His given name was Peter, which, in spite of his mother's honorable intentions, was immediately increased to Peter Rabbit among his associates in Spencer. Not content with well enough, or perhaps inspired by his youth, they soon took up the diminutive. Then, because he was genuinely likeable, Bunny was shortened to Bun, which stuck.

There are limits to compassion in such groups as these. A part of Bun's popularity owed to his unswerving devotion to a good loser. The stakes were small. Still, when Bun's pocket change was gone, he sat back and grinned, listened, perhaps, but did not talk at all.

He was a mucker in the livery stable, employed by Barney, who ran the stables. Barney had grown up on an Iowa farm and knew horses. He also knew cows, pigs and corn, but only horses were relevant to his life in Spencer. The wiry, wizened Barney and Bun were present in their official capacity. They would unhitch, stable and feed the four-horse team that was bringing, though God only knew when, the stage. No freight was expected in that night. The stage ran daily, come hell or high water. Probably there had been some of each, farther up the line.

Ben finished his preparatory book work and the seven seated themselves around the table under the wide-flanged lamp. Barney, with Bun to his left, sat on the bench along the north wall, since neither was fool enough to shed his sheepskin-lined coat, as least before he began to sweat. To Bun's left, at the head of the table, as befits a successful business man, sat Boniface. At Boniface's left, on the other long side of the table was a beefy miner called Golden Gideon, the first section of his name bestowed because he was that rare exception, a successful prospector, the latter for a wholly unrelated reason. He had been lucky in his strike and had held onto it by virtue of his brawn. Since all men do, he must have had a name; but when he described the one book in his eight-by-ten-foot long cabin, he became Gideon. And Gideon he was to remain, at least as long as he stayed in Spencer.

Gideon had thought, he explained when asked about his book, that every home should have a Bible, so he had tucked one into his suitcase when he found one, apparently unused, on a bedside table in the one hotel he'd stayed in while on his way to the gold fields. He said this with such bland sincerity that it became legend even in a town of such traditionless antecedents as Spencer.

Next to Golden Gideon sat the Englishman, known to all and sundry as M'Lord. Save for the regrettable accident of his birth as youngest of eleven children of an earl, the title might have been his. But five older brothers pratically guaranteed that he would never accede to the title. An earlier generation would have referred to him as a remittance man. The frontiersmen among whom he lived substituted the mildly insulting title. He accepted it with as much calm and goodnature as Bun did his identification. Why not?

Next to him sat another Englishman, more humbly born. No one found a title for him; he had to labor under his family name of Felsingham. For lack of other companions even as remotely compatible, the two often shared quarters and took turns hunting for wood to keep them from freezing. As the population burgeoned, fuel receded ever farther from that population's center. The stove side of the table was a little crowded.

Ben sat at the farthest end from Boniface, out of respect for the duties of his office. He was nearest the door. Care of the fire fell to anyone who felt cold. Since Bun and Barney rarely removed their coats and were seated against the north wall and behind the table, that task seldom fell to them. Anyway, neither ever entered without an armful of wood. They paid their dues. Since Ben lived there, and since he usually wore only an open vest over his thick, plaid wool shirt, he was apt to be cold first. He did not hesitate to point out the deficiency to his guests if the woodbox bottom came into view.

The cards were dealt and the room fell silent.

As usual, Bun lasted only a few hands but stayed in his corner because he couldn't get out without disturbing the other players. His feet were cold, but then they usually were from early November until May. His interest in the game was unflagging. In time he would make a good poker player. It just took him a little longer than most.

Felsingham was next to drop out. He went outside and stayed there a little longer than expected. When he returned, Ben swung halfway around to face him. "Hear anything?" he asked.

"Yes," Felsingham replied. "But they're ungodly slow. Sounds like the horses have had it."

The horses had had it. An hour before, they had stopped midway through a drift, and neither strong words nor the blacksnake whip would start them again. Inside the coach four women and two men stirred uneasily. The knew they were not in Spencer. Would they ever get there?

Huddled in the forward facing seat, a buffalo robe tucked around them, were three young women travelling together. In the early part of the journey, when daylight made an adventure of moderate discomfort, they talked in low tones. Occasionally they would change places allowing the one in the center to thaw out a bit. But by the time the horses stopped, the youngest had been afforded the center seat.

The lady opposite them hunched close to her escort, who

maintained his center seat throughout the long drive. Though the other man was dressed in black and wore a clerical collar, Phil Jackson was not one to expose his sister to contact with any man, reverend or profane. The reverend meditated or slept and did not enter the conversation.

Outside the cursing grew louder. The stage jerked forward a few yards and stopped again.

"I'm going out to see if I can be of any help," said the oldest of the three fellow travelers, coming as nearly erect as the low roof of the coach and her generous height would allow. "Thank goodness I'm warmly dressed. Why don't you, Miss Jackson," she nodded across the coach, "sit here with the girls? You'll be much more comfortable."

Miss Jackson, half paralyzed with cold, still moved quickly enough to forestall her brother's interference. The other two, by common consent, gave her the center seat. Their companion was already closing the coach door behind her.

Sam, the relief driver, saw her emerge. "Stay inside," he snapped. Then he added sheepishly, "Unless . . . "

"No, I'm okay," she told him. "It just seemed to me I could do some good out here. Can I?"

"Jake won't like it," Sam said. "But maybe you can get up there in the driver's seat and cluck at the team from time to time. They'll follow us, but there should be somebody holding the lines. Horses know the difference."

"I know," she said, spryly mounting the front wheel and swinging into the seat. The reins had been tied loosely to the brake handle, and she retrieved them efficiently. Sam and Jake walked slowly ahead of the lead team; the horses following obediently.

When they had come out on a ridge blown clear of snow, both men dropped back but did not stop the horses to resume their places. Another drift halted the team, and Jake made acid comment as he took the lead again with Sam. "Getting spoiled, ain't you?" he jeered at the horses. They were too tired to resent his jeer, even if they had understood it. When the way grew easier again, Jake surprised Sam, who had always thought of his partner as a woman hater. He held up his thick fur mittens to the driver. "Put 'em on, Miss," he advised. "They don't get in your way much. And anyway, these nags are too tired to run away."

"Thank you," she answered, and handed down her own knit pair, still warm from her hands.

Things went better after that. In spite of having twice as many legs as the men, the horses travelled no faster. Even Jake knew they were doing what they could, and at last Spencer was near enough so he could catch an occasional glimpse of lights through the snow. The station house sat on one of those providentially windswept spots, and the last quarter of a mile was easy. Comparatively easy, that is.

It was Jake who sang out a grateful "Whoa!" as they came up beside the building. Barney and Bun were there to receive the horses.

"Get inside as quick as you can," Sam told the volunteer. "And thanks. Even the horses know what a help you were."

She nodded and found the door. Sam turned to help the other coach passengers.

Ben was poking more wood into the potbellied stove. He indicated a chair near it. "Tough trip?" he asked with genuine concern, as he took in her snowy head and shoulders.

She smiled and nodded. "I am Pallas Niarchus," she said. "And you?"

"Ben Dormer, station agent," he answered. Must be a real lady if she was that particular about not talking until she was introduced, he thought.

The other passengers crowded inside, bringing with them a blast of cold air. Jake and Sam followed, and without a word, Ben poured each a mug of coffee from the tall, blue enameled pot on the stove.

"Give the lady a cup," Jake suggested gruffly. "We wouldn't be here if it wasn't for her."

Both Ben and Sam stared open-mouthed. Ben said, "Folks, this is Miss Niarchus. Some of you know her, of course. All the rest of us are glad to."

Phil Jackson asked for coffee. Ben poured it without a word, and Phil accepted it without thanks. Miss Niarchus was still without hers.

"I haven't enough cups to go around," Ben apologized in a low voice.

"I don't mind waiting," said Pallas Niarchus. "Do you have just one more cup. Miss Jackson is about frozen."

The dark, bird-like little woman blushed but accepted the freshly washed cup M'Lord held toward her. "Thank you!" she breathed faintly. It was true she was all but frozen.

The ladies did not join the conversation. Having found his offer of a cup accepted, M'Lord gathered those from the poker table and washed them, holding the well-used dishtowel low so the ladies wouldn't see it.

The ladies were not inclined to be critical. M'Lord saw to it that the next cupful went to Pallas Niarchus. Miss Jackson drank hers quickly and returned the cup.

"Not for a refill," she said. "So that someone else can have it. It helped so much. Thank you!"

Ms. Niarchus' blonde companion spoke without being introduced. "Nellie and I can share one."

Whatever the three were, Boniface throught shrewdly, they certainly were good sports.

When M'Lord handed the cup to the blonde, she murmured thanks, then added, "This is Nellie Wood and I am Catherine Knight."

"Edward Strathmore," said M'Lord. "I'm happy to make your acquaintance."

He returned to his usual corner behind the stove, out of his element and not seeking it after his many years as an outsider. Miss Niarchus watched him, her scrutiny discreet. Her discretion had not hindered her earning her living — even in the way she had chosen.

Boniface stood up and reached for his sheepskin. "Anyone for the hotel?" All the women, plus the two male passengers, stood up.

"Looks like you've got them all," Ben told him.

Papa and the Pig

Edith M. Bateman
Mankato, Minnesota

I close my geography book, pile my school books neatly, bind them with a strap and carry them to the shelf behind the parlor stove. Returning to the kitchen, I watch my father. He has pulled the large arm chair close to the kitchen range. The chair is lined with a patchwork quilt which drapes loosely around his shoulder. One leg rests on the open oven door; the other foot he has raised off the drafty floor by placing it on a stick of firewood. The kerosene lamp on the table and the fire flickering in the range cast shadows about the room. With a little imagination they can be anything to me: a circus, spooks, Fourth of July fireworks or, like tonight, they help make a quiet peaceful time, a time for closeness, small talk, even a silence filled with love.

I watch as he lays the hone on his knee, dampens it with oil and makes the first circular movements with the knife. He is a little man, short and thin and very old. He had fallen from the apple tree as a child and broke both arms. The doctor set them, but when the casts were removed Papa could not straighten either arm. They are slightly curved, looking like a bird ready for flight. His arms are short and his shirt sleeves inches too long, so he wears arm bands. The elastic bands are tight around Papa's arms just above his elbows, and his blue cotton work shirt blouses over the bands. His everyday arm bands are cut from bulk elastic, but he has fancy blue ones for Sundays. He wears long sleeves and underwear winter and summer. In summer they are cotton one-piece underwear, but now he has changed to his long, bulky wool ones. Bib overalls hang loosely from his thin shoulders.

His health is poor, and as I watch him draw the knife against the hone, I can read the pain in his face. Rheumatism rakes every bone in his body. He is never far from his tin of Dr. Miles pain pills. Tonight his lips as well as his tongue and teeth are a vivid pink from the many pills. It is the weather, I conclude. The October wind is raw and Papa complains when the days are cold and damp. The heat from the stove warms the kitchen, but the rest of the house is cold. We must not start the parlor stove for another month or the wood we have chopped will not last until spring.

"Is tomorrow the day?" I ask, my eyes glued to the knife with its rasping sound as knife and hone come together.

"Yes, tomorrow. We shut the pig in the stall tonight. We fed her early and bedded her down good. She was nervous. I think she knows what we plan to do. Animals understand a lot more than we give them credit for."

"Do you like to kill her, Papa?"

"No, I don't like to kill anything, but that is part of life. We raise chickens, hogs, cows, horses, sheep, ducks and the geese. Everything has a purpose. Some chickens will provide our eggs, some will be killed for meat and some we will keep to raise next year's flock. The cows give us milk or provide our beef. Our horses are work horses. They must earn their keep or we sell them.

He stops honing and looks at me for a long time. "And now," he adds quietly, "now it is time to butcher the pig." He draws his thumb across the knife blade and seems satisfied. He concentrates on the tip. That is the important part, I know.

Finally he lays the knife and hone aside. He holds out a crippled arm and instinctively I snuggle up. "Bedtime, pet," he whispers. It has been said lovingly, but I know it is an order. I stand on tip toe, kiss him, take the soapstone that will warm my bed from the oven and leave for the loft.

At five o'clock Papa's voice echoes up the stairs. "George, time to get up. George! George!"

Grey streaks break through the darkness. I hear the lid clank on the stove. Life on the farm has begun and today I want to see it all. I fight the urge to close my eyes again. The round boards are cold on my bare feet as I grab my clothes and run down to the warmth of the cook stove. My sister Faye has already started the pancakes. I love the white ones, but today it is buckwheat. I will have to eat them; that's all there will be for breakfast, but I don't have to like them.

The barrel stands on stones in the grove. After breakfast we carry wood, light the fire and begin filling the barrel with water. It's a long trek from the well to the barrel. I am assigned the job of pumping. My sister and brother carry the buckets, and my father stands on an old chair and pours the water. It doesn't take long before the water is steaming. Dad says, "OK, kids. It's time."

I run ahead to the barn, and sit on the stairs to the haymow. An awful fear runs through my body as I see Papa examining the knife for the hundredth time. I can see the worry on his face. What if something goes wrong? I want to yell, "Don't do it, Papa," but I know if I say anything I will be sent to the house. George and Papa climb over the wooden side of the pen. They push the pig in the corner, and my brother holds it tight against the wall with his body. Before the pig has a chance to move, Papa gives a mighty thrust and the knife enters the chest and heart. The pig's squeal fills the barn and blood spurts as the knife is twisted and withdrawn. I scamper up the steps to the mow, bury myself in the straw and cry. Not for long though, as now the work must begin and we all have to help.

When the blood has completely drained from the pig it is loaded in the big wooden wheel barrow and taken to the bubbling water barrel. There the back legs are opened and a heavy wooden dowel forced between the tendons and bone. A block and tackle have been mounted to the tree limb. A large hook dangling from the rope sways in the wind.

Papa catches the rope, snags the wooden dowel, and motions for George to raise the pig. When the pig is over the barrel, Dad steadies it and George lowers the pig into the boiling water. Dad keeps testing the hair on the pig and when it is just the right temperature, George again raises the pig. Both men shave the pig and then gut it. The intestines are put in the large dishpan. Faye and I take them to the well to wash, turn inside out and then wash again. They will be used for sausage. We do not have a smoke house, but the neighbor has agreed to buy them from us to use with his own. We clean the heart and liver. The rest of the innards will go for chicken feed. The inside of the pig is washed down with clean water several times, cut in half lengthwise, and left hanging to cool.

Three extra leaves are put in the big kitchen table which we cover with oilcloth and several layers of newspapers. The meat grinder is securely screwed on one corner. George carries in half of the hog, and Papa carefully saws it into smaller pieces. Faye and I cut the scrap pieces, and run them through the grinder for sausage. It's greasy meat, and the raw meat smell makes my stomach feel funny. When both halves are cut and ground, we carry the roasts to the basement. Papa has filled the big crock jar with salt and water. He takes an egg from the crate and says, "I wonder if it is strong enough."

"How will you know?" I ask.

He stirs the salt water with a long stick, then drops the egg, shell and all, into the mixture. It sinks to the bottom and then slowly comes to the top again. "Yes, when a raw egg floats it is good. It's ready to receive the meat." All the roasts and the pork slabs are put in the brine, topped with a wooden cover and weighted down with a rock.

Upstairs Faye is busy frying sausage patties. They will be layered in a crock jar, the hot lard poured over them. When they are cool and the lard hard, they will be covered and taken to the basement. I know that each morning this winter three or four patties will be dug out of the lard, warmed and eaten with our pancakes, or maybe a slab will be taken from the brine, cut into strips, dipped in milk and flour, and fried to a crisp brown. This will have a heavy rind that we will chew and chew to get all the flavor before it is finally discarded.

It has been a full day's work, and we are all tired. Dad nods to the messy table, "Clean it up, Edith. George and I will go milk and do the chores. I'll bring some fresh milk in with me, and we'll have some bread soup for supper. I'm too tired to eat much tonight. The warm milk will be good for all of us."

I begin rolling the greasy papers and feeding them in the stove. "Pee-you! What is that smell?" I ask Faye. She grins, and opens the oven door. There on a baking pan lies the hog's tail.

"We can't waste anything," she said. "You can eat bread soup, but I'm going to have pork for my supper!"

excerpts from
Farm Interlude

Marjorie Myers Douglas
Edina, Minnesota

W hen there was an opportunity for our children to become sheep farmers, we welcomed it as a chance for them to learn the business of farming. This is how it came about.

Art Sackreiter was a close friend of my husband. He ran the coop grain elevator in nearby Milan, and he always made it worth our while to move our grain through him. "We never got the top dollar on the market," my husband says now, "but always close to it."

But just this once Art had made a mistake—and a bad one.

He had invested in a fine young flock of two hundred and fifty Hampshire sheep and placed them on shares with a farmer who had then moved to woods country in northern Minnesota. The usual arrangement is for the owner to get half the wool clip and half the lambs, but for three years Art had received nothing. The renter had no phone, letters went unanswered, and Art's duties at the elevator never let up. He had no chance to get away to see what was happening.

One morning early in April of 1955 Art pulled into the yard in a vast semi- trailer truck and began to work on Don—in his sidelong, indirect way—to go with him to repossess the sheep. Don protested that his planter still lacked a final adjustment and timing, while the fuel injector for the "M" tractor, a touchy thing to install, needed his personal attention. "But where did you get the semi?"

"That independent trucker from Dawson came in and unloaded his grain and began yelling like usual, 'I'm sick of this job. I need to go fishing and forget all about it.' "

"Well, do it!" Art had replied. "Take my car, and I'll take your semi and reclaim my sheep."

Early Saturday morning found him in our driveway with the children running out to see what was going on. Anne was a rosy, impulsive twelve-year-old. Bill, nine, was an easygoing, faithful understudy for his dad, and Bruce at three was all big, earnest blue eyes under the bobbing ball fringe of his Mexican hat.

When he realized Don was really refusing to accompany him, Art "allowed as how" he did not know how to turn the ungainly thing around. He sounded forlorn when he said he'd have to go on alone. Don climbed in, pulled the big rig farther into the driveway and maneuvered it into position. I didn't really know until afterward that Don had never driven a semi before. Perhaps Art was sly enough to get him behind the wheel on purpose—counting on that thrill to help persuade Don to go along. Certainly Art was not skilled as an operator of big machinery, and I could see that Don felt concern for him. (I don't doubt that our friend had counted on this, too.)

At any rate, Don agreed to go, and as soon as that was decided, Art began trying to interest him in taking the sheep on shares for him. Don flatly refused, saying he did not want any more stock.

"You have room for them, don't you, on your river pasture or the small pasture? It's a shame for rich meadow like that to go to waste."

"I don't want them, Art. Planting will start next week, and I've got to get four hundred acres of corn in and another four hundred of soy beans."

"I'll give you easy terms, and these ewes are good sound Hamps," he urged.

"Cash is short right now, and there's gas, seed, fertilizer and wages, and it's a long time until harvest. No sheep! And that's final!"

It was late afternoon before they found the right village and, far out on a woods road, finally located the renter's place. No one was at home, so the weary men used the well-trained stock dog and rounded up the sheep into the dooryard. Just then the wife returned. As she came toward them in her shabby jeans, she gave a small hand signal, and the waiting dog burst into action scattering the animals in every direction. Art abruptly told her, and her silent, stooped husband who now joined them, to have the sheep in the lot early next morning or he would call the sheriff.

Next day they sorted off all the ewes, then added ewe lambs

to make up for the ones which had died and the five registered bucks which were missing. Generously, Art divided the remaining lambs with a couple so they could build up a bunch of their own.

When they were nearly home, Art asked Don what the flock was worth. Don knew the sheep market. He calculated a moment and named a good figure. They had been well cared for and had no doubt produced a handsome income for the thieving farmer. Again Art wheedled Don to buy the sheep and, when Don still refused, confessed that he had no place to put them. He begged for temporary pasture, which, of course, was granted. Then he made a final proposition in a way which could not be turned down.

"Buy them for your children. Nothing down. Let the kids pay for the flock out of their share of the wool and lambs, and there'll be no interest on the principal. You'll be doing me a big favor!"

How could a father refuse?

Thus Art had what he had been cleverly angling for from the time he had driven over the previous morning, and the children had a project of their own.

* * *

The children looked forward to lambing, and so did I. We pictured cuddly little Christmas card creatures gamboling about in the sunshine. In reality some were born as early as February when even the sunny days were very cold and frost outlined the cracks of the shed with white. Some came in frigid rains or in March snow storms. To my surprise many came into our kitchen chilled, wet and dirty, needing to be warmed near the oven, rubbed with a towel, and bottle-fed before being returned to their mothers in the sheds. First-time mothers sometimes had to be helped to claim their little ones by penning them in close quarters to enforce bonding. But once a lamb had nursed, it could safely be removed to the cozy kitchen for a short time without endangering family ties.

Only one lamb was permanently abandoned that first season. What pride I felt as that bedraggled little creature began to respond to the warmth and the feedings. She stood on her blanket in her carton and butted and wriggled with joy as she drank.

46

Her tail, which would later be docked, rotated rapidly in total bliss. It might have been a crank that powered the feeding process, and it scarely missed a beat.

Total involvement with one little lamb can be tiresome, however, and she did not like being returned to the shed. By Easter, which was almost the end of April that year, she was a husky youngster of thirty-five pounds or so though she looked much larger with her curly grey coat and smooth black face. Easter Sunday dawned in a dreary drizzle after several days of rain, and the feed lot was hopelessly muddy. Don finished heavy chores early, and the boys' faces shone above their blazers and Eton collared shirts from their hasty baths. Anne was radiant in the lacy red dress Grammy Lynn had crocheted for her. Breakfast was cleaned up in short order, and the good smell of beef roast already escaped the oven. Don, in raincoat and rubbers, brought the car to the nearest gate for us. When he pulled up, I opened the door and turned to help Anne with the umbrella. Before we could draw breath Baabaa, the orphan, had scrambled up the concrete steps and clattered into the kitchen.

We never fed her inside anymore, but here she was wet to the point of dripping, her fur matted with mud and straw. She skidded, she skipped, her tiny hooves made grubby streaks across the shiny linoleum. She bumped against the white enamel of the stove, and left her imprint there in grey and black. Recognizing Anne, who had frequently fed her, Baabaa lunged toward her, and with an agile leap to the corner the girl barely escaped.

"Open the door!" I yelled. Bruce and Bill and I tried to shoo the befuddled beast out without touching her, but again she stubbornly dashed and skidded in the wrong direction. Visions of filthy hands and ruined clothing replaced white lilies and Easter music in our minds as the precious minutes were wasted in the ridiculous performance.

Don was unaware of our plight, and we heard him tap on the horn to remind us that he was due in the choir. Time was growing short. In desperation I leaned far forward, grabbed deeply into the nasty, smelly wet wool and, pushing and pulling, maneuvered the determined animal out onto the stoop and down the steps. I hung on while the youngsters made their get away. A quick handwash, and we were in the car without any visible sign of our adventure—although I could detect a faint skunk-like aroma through my best white gloves. As we drove off, Don had the courage to joke that, after this he would have to count heads when his family came out of the kitchen door just to be sure what he let into the car.

Who Needs Geritol When a List Will Do

Ailys Henningson
Ortonville, Minnesota

Mom kept lists
    on scraps of paper
    tucked in books
    and other out of the way places,
    lists of her grandchildren
    from the oldest to the youngest.
So it was that Chris Robert always headed the list,
and John Fredrick was always the last.

I guess, come to think of it, I keep lists too.
    They are all around me;
        the pad on the kitchen counter
            records needed grocery items,
        the calendar on the wall
            marks the birthdays for the month,
        the magnetic notes fastened on the refrigerator
            remind me of important meetings
                and appointments
                I dare not miss.

I'd never function without my lists.
My mind is full of them.
I lay awake nights
    marshalling my lists in line,
        this I must do tomorrow,
            and then this,
            and this . . .

Seems Like There's Nothing To Eat Around Here
from My Diary

Viola V. Rostad
Erhard, Minnesota

I was seven years old the year Charles Lindbergh flew alone across the Atlantic, eight the year Mama bought navy blue straw cloche hats for sister Marcie and me. They had grosgrain ribbon around the brim which went stylishly very low over our foreheads. That Christmas we found little rooms of doll furniture under the Christmas tree with celluloid dolls (a bit oversized) sitting on the delicate padded chairs. When I was nine years old in 1929 something happened to the country. The banks closed, they said, and Dad lost some money, but not much because we hadn't much. I began to hear dire stories at the dinner table — all caused by the * + x@* Reds, my Dad said. Rich men began to jump out of windows in New York City — or someplace.

We worked extra hard in the garden that summer. Ma raised a flock of turkeys, and we got a fine new ivory and blue kitchen stove with the proceeds. Ma made school clothes for us out of old clothes from the wooden trunk — clothes she had saved from before she was married, when she was thinner. We had to be satisfied with penny pencils and narrow Big Chief tablets, and Dad bought orange shoes for us from a vendor on the streets of Wahpeton. The shoes had paper soles and disintegrated as soon as they were wet. Our overshoes were made of heavy canvas and buckled four and five high. They got wet fast, so every winter night overshoes were drying by the stove.

Mama got pale and thin that winter and, for the first time ever, Dad took her in the Model T Ford to Wahpeton to have her baby, my sister Charmeon. It was midwinter and Mama came home looking worn out, with beautiful, thin, blue-veined hands. Dad bought oranges for Charmeon that winter as he had learned about vitamins, but the rest of us got our vitamin C from canned tomatoes.

50

By the spring of 1930, even we children could see something was very wrong with our world. The spring rains didn't come — nor the summer or fall rains. Sometimes the lightning flashed and the thunder rolled, but then faded away. The crops didn't grow, and the entire family desperately carried water to a withering garden. Then the wells began to go dry, and Dad and my brothers tried to dig one out among the cottonwood trees. They dug down to water, but it was not enough to pump out — so we had to take cream cans to the neighbors to bring back cooking and drinking water. I never knew what it was to be thirsty until then.

Marcie and I went exploring near our country school one day. It was late summer by this time and we had come to look over an old dump ground. Along with rusty tin cans and old medicine bottles, we found the remains of bright blue and white dishpans, tea kettles and coffeepots, enameled cookware of a generation gone by. Then we heard a desperate, constant call, "Pete, Pete, Pete," which seemed to come from the direction of the girl's toilet at the schoolhouse. We rushed over and, down in the toilet hole (dry now after the long hot summer), was a fluffy baby duck, doomed to die unless rescued. The hole was deep and the opening on the seat not very large, but the thing had to be done. Somehow I wriggled myself down through the hole and dropped to the bottom. I handed the frightened baby duck up to my sister, and then came the challenge of how to get out again. Since it was quite necessary that *this* be done, too, I managed to jump up and get a handhold on the edge of the seat hole, lift my feet up on the earth bank next to the hole and, inch by inch, wriggle my head and shoulders, and then my body, up and out. I felt battered, and my heart pounded, but my long experience of tree climbing had made me strong and agile. We walked home, proudly carrying our little prize, taking turns holding him.

Pete-Pete was our pride and joy, happily following us around until one day he joyously waded in the cold water on the ground near the cottonwoods well. Apparently he caught pneumonia that night, for he died the next day. We grieved for a while. By this time, though, we were long accustomed to both the life and death of animals on the farm. We welcomed baby kittens and buried them when they expired. Lack of food and water took its toll on baby calves, which Dad threw on the manure pile in the winter and burned in the spring along with a dead horse or two. I recall standing out by the plum trees watching the animals burn, the acrid smell of the burning hides offending my nose, but with fascination I watched the rib cage empty and disintegrate. Many of the bones did not burn, however, and Marcie reminded me that we children, Delbert, Marcie and I, put them to good use as time went on. We pretended that each bone was a horse for our ranch, so we each tied several bones to a long string (probably pieces of twine), and pulled them after us. The bones, white and dry, bounced as we galloped along.

We children filled washtubs with dried sticks gathered from the grove of trees to burn for baking bread. We picked up dried cow chips to boil the potatoes in spite of the acrid odor. Dad found new things to eat. Wild mustard and dandelion greens, fresh white puff balls picked quickly in the morning dew and fried in bacon grease. They were excellent, crisp and snowy white, but beware of the puff ball which was not fresh, for it filled quickly with worms. Ma baked pies from the deadly nightshade (Dad found out from somewhere that the idea of poison was an old wive's tale). Ma made jam out of wild ground cherries, and we made a trip to the sand hills to pick choke cherries for sauce.

We spent one long day picking miniscule wild strawberries from a wild prairie meadow. While we were picking, we ate the strawberries, too, and for supper Ma baked a big strawberry shortcake. I remember getting sick that night and vomiting from the over-supply, and brother Clint broke out in hives all over his body the next day — large reddish-white smooth patches which were soothed by poultices of soda and water. It was just as well that Ma used the remaining strawberries to mix with the last of the rhubarb patch because, by winter, they tasted good to us again. We made currant and gooseberry jelly and sauce from our woodland patch and, in early spring, when the Russian thistles were soft and green, we pulled the tender plants to add to beef soup. Every hard, small plum from the bushes was

52

canned. The plums had tough skins but the juice was good with cream mixed in.

Navy beans were easy to grow in spite of the dry weather, so we planted many rows. Then, in late summer, we pulled the dry vines, filled the tin-lined wagon box that sat on the ground, and we got inside with bare feet and stomped the vines until the dry beans fell free. After that, the vines were thrown away and we bagged the beans in flour sacks. It took many painstaking sessions of bean sorting to cull out the blackened and rotting ones from the good ones, but we became experts, each of us spreading out our separate piles on the big round oak table in the kitchen. Then Ma would soak them overnight and simmer them all day with whatever was on hand—a piece of bacon or ham, a pork hock or a piece of salt pork. With onions, salt and pepper and sometimes fresh or canned tomatoes added, it was a tempting, fragrant family meal.

Very little of our precious chicken was wasted. My teenage brothers, Arlie and Clint, boiled chicken feet, peeled off the rough outer coat and chewed on the gristle that was left. (They did the same thing with pig tails, for those two were an adventurous hungry pair.) If the chicken was a laying hen, the soft-shelled egg was retrieved, and half-formed eggs (mostly yolk) were boiled in the chicken stew. Ma also cleaned out the crinkly egg sack and boiled it—perfectly good coarse meat. We ate the heart, the liver and the gizzard but not the kidneys.

We made head cheese from pig's heads and sweetbreads from the brains, but we never ate the blood of an animal. The neighbors who helped butcher would, though. I was very small when I witnessed the horrible sight of a stuck hog running madly round and round, squealing in terror as it lost its life blood. It wasn't supposed to have gotten away at all, but they caught it and retrieved a basin of blood to make blutwurst.

Dad built a smokehouse out back of the old garage. The smokehouse was used to make sausages, bacon and ham. We made the sausages ourselves, cleaning out the intestines of the hog for containers, then cutting up the lesser cuts of meat, grinding and seasoning them, and then stuffing it into the intestine (or gut) of the hog. Dad hung the smoked meat from the kitchen ceiling in cheese cloth for final curing. Winter days in our big yellow kitchen was an experience. The lignite coal fire from the stoves, the wet, manure-covered overshoes from the barn, the smells from the cream separator, unwashed bodies and a damp, sticky floor, mixed to make an odor that was quite rudimentary.

The same kitchen, on a summer's day, took on quite another character with the cream separator sparkling clean, the stove sitting pretty and idle, the floor scrubbed spotless, a fresh oilcloth on the table, the meat consumed and the boots put away, a fresh-baked cake on the table covered with thick whipped cream from the cool storm cellar, and fresh new peas to be shelled. Then the neighbors could be invited over to play whist for the evening, and we would gather in the darkened living room along with our young Uncle Ray and his Norwegian wife, Agnes. We would play Skip to My Lou and Norwegian circle games, even singing in Norwegian which we learned from our aunt. "Ona mata peia, Hesta yet a peda." No, that's not right, but it was a fun song. Uncle Ray and Aunt Agnes had such great singing voices, and we romped to our heart's delight.

These were the early years of the Great Depression, a mixture of making do and fun times. Later it would get worse.

By 1932 we were well into the Depression Era. We lived on a half-section farm near Barney, North Dakota, and already the prairie land was sifting in the everlasting dry wind. Desert-like drifts of gray sand piled near the fence lines and against the buildings with old grass and weeds peeking through. Russian thistles, round and prickly, rolled across the fields and pastures, stacking high against the fence lines until the wind changed and sent them rolling again. The sand felt soft and silky on our bare feet until we stepped on a Russian thistle sticker. Then we had to stand on one foot and pull it off before warily continuing on. The ditches filled with sand and, in time, even fence posts were covered. The sand whitened into a desolate, desert landscape.

Sometimes the sky would darken and savage streaks of lightning darted here and there. The distant thunder would sound, and we'd wait in anticipation for the rains that never came. I can remember the entire family standing in the farmyard anxiously watching this display of weather. In North Dakota one can see from horizon to horizon—the sky was a large part of our lives.

54

Week after week, month after month and, finally, year after year, the rains only teased and threatened, perhaps splashing a few drops to dry in the hot sand but never enough to penetrate and sustain the thirsty earth.

The day came when we were out of flour and salt, so Dad loaded up a sack of precious seed grain, and I pulled on my long blue knit sweater and rode to Barney with him on the high seat of the lumber wagon. The grocer, as usual, gave us a free large sack of bumpy orange-colored peanuts — we didn't eat any until we could share them with everyone at home.

I don't recall ever being *really* hungry. There always seemed to be a hard biscuit in the bread box or a crust of bread but, as I look back, there were sings of malnutrition among us. Mama's babies came harder, and she was pale and sick afterwards. I had aching feet and legs, and often cried with pain as I sat on my bed rocking back and forth. My menstrual periods were a time of agony; my hips seemed to stiffen and I remained home from school on those days. Winter was a time of head and stomach aches, sore throats and colds which we survived with home remedies. But then survival during those days was not only a national but a world-wide struggle, and I suppose our family struggled as valiantly as any. Even at the age of twelve, I recall my father's changing face, the lines deepening on his forehead, his slower walk. He seldom played his violin or strummed on his old banjo. Sometimes, though, in the evening on the porch, I could hear my brothers playing "Old Black Joe" on the harmonica. "I'm a-comin' I'm a-comin' for my head is bending low . . . "

The Assassination

Muriel J. Bergquist
White Bear Lake, Minnesota

S taying ahead of three growing children was a tough challenge for me. Not only did I have to perform as referee and social planner on occasion, but it was also my task to manipulate them into new learning experiences.

For example. To avoid fighting at the dinner table, I made it a rule that we would speak only in French; to lure them on weekend ski trips, I allowed them to bring a friend; so, in order to interest them in politics, I started our own White House family.

Ethel and Bob were the names of the prolific guppies. The lovebirds were Ted and Joan. Jackie was the sensuous cat, and JFK (sometimes called Kennedy) was our jaunty, multi-breed dog. Whenever we added to our animal kingdom, choosing the name was dealt with seriously.

So whenever Ethel and Bob produced a new batch of guppies, or Ted plucked Joan's feathers in a rage, or JFK went on a week-long prowl, it became a real-life drama to us all. Jackie, of course, never did anything except preen herself from morning until night. She was the only one who was a bore.

On November 22, 1963, I was driving home from monitoring recess at school. At first I didn't pay much attention to the urgent radio message until the words "guns shots from an abandoned building" penetrated my thoughts. Rushing into the house, I turned on the T.V. and watched in horror as the assassination story unfolded.

When the kids came home after school, I waited until they were comfortable in play clothes and having their cookies and milk before I announced the news.

"Kennedy's dead," I blurted out tearfully.

There was such a howl of grief that I stopped crying and watched them in shock. Was I raising emotionally disturbed children? What had I done to make them so overly sensitive?

Just then, with one ear flopping and tail held high, JFK marched across the yard and squeezed through his personal door into the kitchen. The children stopped in amazement.

"We thought you said Kennedy was dead," they accused as they threw themselves on him.

So in our family we never did treat Kennedy's assassination with the proper respect it fully deserved. By the time we finally worked through the confusion of names, his assassinator was assassinated and the long, sad weekend was over.

I was the one who finally learned a lesson. From then on, dogs were named Boy or Girl, cats were called Kitty, regardless of gender, and everything else remained nameless.

FALLEN APPLES: DOING BATTLE

The Undiscovered Land
from the novel The Time of Love

Joseph P. O'Hara
Rollingstone, Minnesota

I remember when we first went into combat in October of 1944; I saw my first dead body. It lay on a farm just east of the German-Dutch border: a young German soldier, his gray-green uniform blending with the still, green grass, lay under an apple tree. He lay sprawled on his back surrounded by rotting apples; with sightless eyes he stared at the few apples still hanging from the leafless tree.

> Fallen Apples
> Rotting
> Red
> Shattered human
> Ashen
> Dead.
> Deutschland grown,
> Deutschland bred,
> Evanescent
> Lonely
> Bled.

Although I was to see many dead after that time, that first sight always stayed with me. In short order dead American and German bodies became a common fact of life. We workers in this abattoir got over our early queasiness and accepted them as part and parcel of this strange landscape. This edge of Germany had been a place of mud, blood, filth and destruction. The red-tiled roof, brick villages were all shattered. After months of combat this small area resembled a WWI battlefield.

Initially we stayed in one location near Palenberg, Germany. The war, other than an occasional brief firing mission, became deja vu: two hours guard duty, four hours off; the continuing argument over who set the guard wrist watch ahead so they could shorten their duty. I explored the German towns. The

Nazi party had removed all the inhabitants from the cities and towns in the area. A large house I went through had red velvet wall paper. It must have belonged to a mine owner or a high Nazi official. I tore a piece off the wall and sent it home in one of my letters to my parents.

In the middle of November the Regiment again went on the attack. The weather went bad at the same time. Incessant rain turned everything gray and dark. The unharvested fields of beets and cabbages putrefied. With the advance we moved forward a mile into a sugar beet field. We set our guns up in the rain and tried to sleep under gun tarps that lay on the ground. Our gun position was surrounded by sprawled dead German and American soldiers. The German bodies had been robbed; circling each body was a scattering of its papers and valueless personal belongings left by the looters. The rotting bodies joined the stench of the decaying beets – a sweet, sickening smell permeated everything. Most of the dead lay on their backs staring at the sunless sky – their mouths open. That night we stood guard duty. "Nerves" Pemberton, a fellow private from Oregon, claimed the bodies moved at night. One German body lay on its back half in and half out of a shallow machine gun pit. The head of the body seemed to have died in the middle of a terrorized scream – it lay in such a manner that the head was flung back and was still two feet off the ground. The long hair hung down toward the ground and swayed slowly back and forth in the wind – the only movement among the motionless corpses.

The custom was that the American bodies lay untouched until recovered by the Grave Registration Teams. I noticed that a dead American Second Lieutenant's wedding ring was missing from his hand the second or third day we were in this position. My number one suspect was our former mortician, now a wire man – a coarse, uncouth private from Pennsylvania.

At first we heard rumors of high casualties and then in a few days the actual details came to us of serious losses. All of us in Cannon Company came from line companies. This friend or that killed or wounded. We were surrounded by empty gray drabness: dark brownish mud, reddish brick rubble, stunted trees, stripped of leaves and bark, shattered villages. Each moment of quiet was ominous – one was always listening, waiting for something, listening when this or that noise began, listening more intently when the sound ceased. We were on the brink of something – teetering on the edge of some abyss. The darkness was gathering about us and we were about to fall – isolated – alone. The separation from our past and the confrontation with the black void of our future drew us together – to try to escape the empty nothingness of ourselves. For the first time I looked at my fellow soldiers as human beings. I began to accept them for what they were. They no longer looked down on me and my pedantic ways, and I no longer looked down on them for their bawdiness. We were comrades, co-conspirators against this hostile world that surrounded us. Death was our enemy. We had come from a world where one lived forever; the termination of it was way off on the horizon of tomorrows; abruptly we were faced with the finality of it – now.

It was these memories that put me on a plane at Minneapolis International Airport in May of 1983. As we flew towards Germany, I put my earphones on to program number #6 "Wunsch-konzert" and heard may of the tunes of the war years: the "Tara Theme" from *Gone With The Wind*, "Chatanooga Choo Choo," "As Time Goes By," "In the Mood," "Begin the Begine," "Maria Elena," "Moonlight Serenade," "Stardust," and "Deep Purple." After an uneventful flight we landed at the Frankfurt airport right on time and with little delay and much walking, cleared customs. I purchased German postage stamps for two of my stamp collecting children. I then went downstairs and picked up my bag. The car rental desk was my next stop. There I was directed to an Opel Kadette. I had requested a VW Rabbit or a Ford Escort.

I found my way out of the airport area and on to autobahn #3 to Cologne. The road was full of Mercedes and Audis. I drove between 120 km (72 mph) and 140 km (84 mph) and they whizzed by me like rockets. The countryside was green and beautiful. Their spring was ahead of ours by three or four weeks. In Minnesota the trees were only in bud; here they had leafed out. By 1:00 p.m. I was on the battlefields of Dueren, Julich, and Linnich. I could not find the little villages whose names were as familiar to me as those of my children: Wurm, Beeck, Puffendorf, Welz, Ruhrdorf, Flossdorf, Tetz, Boslor, Hottorf — and then suddenly, after driving aimlessly for an hour, I stumbled on Tetz, the first village we had taken after crossing the dreadful river on February 23, 1945.

I drove down its narrow streets. It was much bigger than I recalled. There was no sign of war here. No broken roofs, gutted rooms, pockmarked walls. I came to a dead end and saw a man and woman, my age, working on the flowerbeds of their neat house. I stopped and called out: "Hello — hello." They both came over to my car window. I attempted to talk to them in German — it was a failure. I asked if they spoke English; they didn't. The woman left abruptly, murmuring, "Amerikaner." The man's face, I suddenly realized, was horribly scarred and distorted — he looked like some leering skull one sees in a medieval painting. I was startled and uncomfortable. I wanted to drive away from him quickly but I couldn't — he earnestly gave me directions to Flossdorf and Ruhrdorf. I turned around and escaped from Tetz.

I remembered that two Platoons of E Company had been on either side of the town. At one time, they'd been shooting at each other thinking they were the enemy. When I last was in this village, disheveled prisoners were standing in its street — there were seven or eight of them. Their full heads of hair, blown by the wind, hung in strands over their faces. They were being searched, and their watches and wallets were taken from them by their captors — the rewards of winning. That night, in 1945, I had slept fitfully in a basement somewhere in this village.

I followed the scarred man's directions and began to cross the quiet Roer River at Linnich. It was about two o'clock in the afternoon. I saw two old red-faced men, one with his arm over the other's shoulders, staggering on the sidewalk that crossed the bridge. Were they war comrades having their own reunion? I waved but they did not see me. I had never been in Linnich before, but the name was familiar. Linnich was captured on December 2, 1944, by my Regiment after five days of fighting and with heavy casualties. The two villages of Rurdorf and Flossdorf were just below Linnich. They were taken the following day.

These offense successes (if they can be called that) cost the Division 576 KIA's and 1,726 wounded. My own regiment suffered 274 dead. It had been a five-by-seven-mile slaughtering ground.

It was a place, that since 1944, I could neither forget or escape. It was my yesterday, and my today. It is my tomorrow—my undiscovered land.

Wild as the Winds

Ken K. Kelly
Austin, Minnesota

J ust before my 17th birthday in March, 1910, I had hired out
in Austin, Minnesota, as a brakeman on the Milwaukee Railroad. It was two years later in the summer of 1912, when, early
one morning, I was notified by the call boy to work as hind
brakeman on train Number 90 going east to La Crosse, Wisconsin. While I walked to work that beautiful morning, the horizon
lost its golden luster as the sun pushed back the dawn. Dangling dew drops glistened from petals of brightly colored
flowers and saturated the lush lawns of the neighborhood.

I reported to the conductor at the yard office, received my instructions, took the weigh bills, and proceeded to the caboose.
My first duties were to sweep the caboose and bring in ice and
water. Then I prepared the switch lists which showed the merchandise lineup of each of the cars. Meanwhile, the head brakeman coupled up the engine to our train, and the engineer
pumped up the air into the trainline for brake control. I watched
as the air needle slowly inched up to 70 pounds of air pressure,
the amount required by law to ensure the safety of our train.
When the needle on the air gauge reached 70 pounds, I stepped
out of the caboose and swung my arms back and forth across the
front of my body signaling the engineer to set up the brakes. I
walked the full length of the train to make sure all the brake
cylinders and break shoes had set up properly. I noticed the
break shoes cleaving tightly to the wheels of each car. They
seemed welded in a piece of iron, like a dog not wanting to release its hold on a bone. The gleaming cylinders, a necessary
part of the braking system, came out, exposed from the casings
which housed them, indicating that everything was in working
order. Reaching the engine, I passed a few friendly remarks
back and forth with the engineer.

Then I retraced my steps to the caboose to give the air brake
release signal. As I walked, I made sure that the hand brake
chains were hanging limply, as they should, from their hangers.
I didn't want to overlook a single car with a set hand brake that

might cause a flat spot on the wheels as the train moved forward on our journey.

Flat spots could make the wheels pound the rails and break them, thereby causing a derailment. After the head brakeman, fireman and engineer had observed my highball signal, given by extending my arm high overhead and waving it back and forth in an arc, the engineer released the brakes and whistled off two long blasts. I watched as the sleek cylinders on the caboose retracted smoothly and quietly back into the sleeve, where they nestled away from my view. The brake shoes fell away from the wheels and we quickly pulled out of the switching yards and began our trip to La Crosse.

It was ideal weather with cool breezes blowing for what promised to be a perfect run. We set out and picked up cars at each town along the way. I felt thankful to be blessed with an alert mind, quick reflexes and the sure footedness of a cat.

Soon we had left the last town and were starting to descend gradually from the ridge toward Root River Valley, Fountain Hill, and Isinours Junction. It was a two percent grade, a twisting snake-like ride for six miles that included ten different curves. We were gaining speed gradually, which was only natural going down the steep grade to the valley floor below.

All at once the swaying of the caboose became more intense. I wondered if something was amiss. About a mile out of Fountain Hill we hit the first curve. I scrambled to the cupola and looked out the window to see the train from a better vantage point. The eighteen eastbound, freight-laden cars were swaying like the caboose, perhaps even more.

As I gazed out the small window, I suspected there was something wrong with the air in the train line, which was controlled by the engineer's use of a brake valve to set up the shoe brakes for making contact with the wheels. The cars swayed crazily as I vaulted the steps of the cupola, down into the interior of the caboose. The engineer let out a distress signal, one long wailing blast of the whistle, indicating brake failure. Now I knew the train had lost complete use of its air brakes.

As I made my way to the brake staff at the end of the caboose, I was thrown to the floor. "Damn," I blurted as I scrambled to my feet and hurried out the door to set the wind-up chain brake.

After I cinched up the brake and the wheels began squealing, I bounded up the ladder to the roof. I leaped onto the top of the car next to the caboose and prepared to set that hand brake.

I tried to block the feelings of doom that threatened to cloud my mind as I saw the we were out of control, headed for what appeared to be certain disaster. I hurried along the catwalk that runs the length of the cars and cleared the gap between cars in one leap while my brain reeled from what might lay only a breath away. I knew there had been several wrecks on this hill; four or five men had been killed in pileups. I looked toward the engine and saw the head brakeman on top of the head car. He too was setting brakes.

I sensed an insidious evil in the dark shadows of the cliffs we brushed past. The train was going around one curve into a straight away stretch, then sweeping out ahead into another curve. The swaying of the box cars as we gained speed, combined with the up and down bobbing movements, was almost too much to endure. The jerking would smooth out for a few brief seconds, then begin again because the tracks were uneven in places. I walked in a crouched fashion, keeping my body at low center of the box cars. Adrenaline pumped through my body, giving me strength beyond my recognition. I tried to anticipate each move as I made my way from one box car to the next, setting up and spinning each small wheel like mad as I went.

We flashed by Ryan's water tank halfway down the hill. By this time I knew the engineer had horsed over the engine, reversing the drive wheels to help slow us down. A monotonous chug-chug-chug, chug-chug-chug sounded from the engine. The engineer pinched up the valves to those precious brakes located on the engine. He released and set them every few seconds; a constant pressure would have caused the break shoes to crystalize and be of no use at all. He was doing everything in his power to save the day.

Large belches of smoke billowed from the smokestack. The engineer opened sand valves to spew small glistening grains of sand out onto the rails for added traction, an anticlimatic effort of little value since the wind continually swept the gleaming rails clean. The engine was in the throes of evulsion; a deep-throated puffing, hissing sound emerged as though it gasped its last. As we went headlong down two ribbons of steel, I wondered if the engine would hold together.

The wheels cleaved precariously to the rails as they chorused a rythmic chatter to the tune of clickety clack, clickety clack, it's taking me back, it's taking me back. At this juncture in my young life, I wondered if the Lord was preparing to call me home. The sweet sound of flowing motion from the engine, along with the thrust of the main rod on the drive wheels, had been thrown out of sync by the engineer reversing the lever. What had sounded sweet and harmonious before seemed now in the throes of labor pains.

My ears rang from the incessant pounding. The rushing wind tore at my clothes and clawed at my face. It would have been easier to jump off at the first onset of danger, but I would not have been able to live with myself. A born fighter, I wasn't about to let the crew down. Sparks flew, and licking flames spewed from the break shoes like a giant sparkler as steel clung to steel. The train was like a coiled cobra, its bared fangs ready to strike.

At one point, as I timed my leap from one swaying car to another, I lost my balance and rolled to the side. "God," I cried out as I went over the edge. "Dam the air," I shouted at the top of my lungs in the next breath. The wild winds reached out to snare me as I lashed out to the iron rod that ran the length of the box car, the only car so fashioned because it was a live poultry car. Going over the edge, I caught hold of the rod with both hands and hung on with all the strength I could muster. I held and pulled myself up onto the top of the car, then lay there to let strength flow back into my aching body.

I had to tie brakes on as many cars as possible because we still had to make one final, treacherous curve at the bottom of the run, along the bluff and on the straight-away into town. My lungs burned as I gulped deep breaths of air. Finally, I pushed myself to my feet and hurried as fast as I could, spinning hand brakes and putting my feet against the brake staff at the base of the ratchet to hold each brake up tight. Bluffs of yellow soil, rock formations with stoney ledges, and boulders jutted out of mute, ominous bluffs and loomed over the tracks in a blur as we raced out of control down the hill. Brake shoes squealed as they closed up tight against the wheels.

After I had done all I could, I watched the curve on the west side of Isinours Junction. When I saw it, I lay down on the catwalk, hugged it as tight as I could, and prayed.

The engine and lead cars lurched through the sweeping curve. I prayed I would also. The cars made a sickening, squealing noise, and the break shoes smoked, giving off a dull red glow as we careened around the curve and raced on into the flat countryside and the valley below. We didn't stop until we were beyond the depot and switch at Isinous Junction. After the trian came to a halt, I lay on top of the box car for I don't know how long. I was completely drained and saturated with sweat.

Lying there my mind drifted back to when I was nine years old. I was going home from school and had decided to take a short cut through a pasture. Suddenly I felt I wasn't alone as I walked and I let out a cry as I whirled around. In a split second, I took off full tilt. An angry bull was bearing down on me. The barbed wire fence seemed so very far away. I ran as fast as my legs could carry me. I was almost out of breath, my legs growing weary. I thought I couldn't make it, so I dropped the sweater I was carrying, hoping to distract him. When the fence finally loomed in front of me, I flung myself onto the ground and quickly rolled under that haven of safety, tearing my pants and bruising my pride in the process. I looked up at the bull from the other side of the fence. He had pulled up short of where I lay on the ground. His large, ominous eyes glared straight at me as he snorted and pawed the ground near me.

The stench of burning break shoes filled my nostrils and brought me out of the memory, back to the now-still train. After a few minutes I got up, sat on the catwalk of the car I was on, and looked out at the peaceful meadow that lined the road bed and right-of-way. The wild flowers were breathtakingly beautiful. I watched some cows, unaware of what had just happened, munch on the lush green grass that spread out before me. The stillness and the beauty of the day was suddenly punctuated by the song of a meadow lark and I thanked God to be alive. The loveliness of that scene will always be with me.

The fireman sat, like me, in stunned silence. He was too weak even to stand up. Finally, he started to move about the cab of the engine. Then he noticed the engineer slumped at the throttle. The depot agent came running to see what had happened and we sent him scurrying for assistance. We surmised that the engineer had a heart attack, which was confirmed by a doctor a few days later. He remained away from work most of the summer. Standing beside the black, skinned workhorse that gleamed in the bright sunlight, I patted her side and mused, "It was a hell of a ride old girl," as steam hissed from the cylinder cocks. Engine boiler sounds from the steel belly deep from within kept up a steady, deep-throated spasm like thump-thump, thump-thump, thump-thump, as if it was gasping its last. Beautiful sounds, they echoed in my ears.

The fireman, headbrakeman and I worked nearly an hour to release the hand brakes on each car. In one instance it took two of us pulling and tugging at the staff to unlock the brake's death hold. Finally, we were able to move the train slowly back to the depot platform.

The runaway train hadn't been the only accident of the day. The conductor had communed with nature right there on the steps of the caboose. He now sat slumped on the caboose steps, a death-grip hold on the grab irons. I literally had to pry his fingers off. He retired from railroad service that same afternoon and was never seen again.

Later, reflecting on that harrowing ride down Fountain Hill, I realized with a chill how fortunate we had been that none of the brakebeams on the cars had broken as the train sped out of control. As it was, we had attained unbelievable speeds, and only God knows how we negotiated some of those curves on that two percent grade, for six miles down Root River Valley.

One of a series of stories Ken K. Kelly has written about his father, Roy Noble Kelley.

The Longest Month of My Life

Frances Lillo O'Shea
Bagley, Minnesota

When I enlisted in the WAAC (Women's Army Auxiliary Corps) in June, 1943, I was sent to Fort Snelling, Minnesota, to join a group of women from the upper Midwest, all designated for Daytona Beach, Florida, for basic training. We came in every size, shape and nationality, but we had several things in common. We were all young, all volunteers, and all of us were among the first American women ever to wear their country's uniform.

The journey south took four days, as we were often shunted onto sidings to allow trains carrying troops and ammunition to roar through. Anything that could roll on rails was pressed into service during the war, but the train the army loaded us on in Jacksonville, Florida, for the run down the coast to Daytona Beach could only have come from a junkyard. It was stinky, dirty and stifling hot. There was no drinking water on board. When we finally pried open the windows, the coach was immediately filled with billowing, choking black smoke from the engine.

The run finally ended in a railroad yard in Daytona Beach. We stumbled out on the tracks, sooty, sweaty, rumpled and gasping for air. I had wanted to look nice for our arrival, so I had saved a gay full skirt and white peasant blouse for the arrival. As I staggered across the tracks, hopping on one foot, trying to dislodge cinders from my open sandals, I looked like I had crawled out of a rat hole. Hell could not be any hotter than Florida in June.

Our new camp had been hastily built in a swamp. Truckloads of dirt had been hauled in to build up a road system; then the barracks were set on stilts so their front doors would open onto the road. God only knows what lived in the marsh beneath us! Our first lecture that evening was on "the identification of the coral snake and how to treat its poisonous bite." We stepped gingerly on our way home.

The army wasted no time in issuing uniforms and getting rid

of our civilian clothes. We passed in long lines down a supply depot, calling out our sizes as we went. There was no chance to try anything on; what you got was what you wore. When we staggered out the back door, we had shoes dangling by their laces from around our necks, three hats perched one on top of the other on our heads, and arms spread wide, piled high with uniforms, shirts, ties, underwear, pajamas, robes, and coats. Our visored caps resembled those worn during the Civil War and were dubbed "Hobby Hats" after Colonel Hobby, the first WAAC Commander. They were not becoming. At least our fatigue clothing was comfortable—it was the outfit we wore most of the time for training. Unlike our skirts, the fatigue dresses were short-sleeved, buttoned down the front, and made from green and white striped seersucker which didn't have to be ironed. Under the dress we wore matching bloomers.

The only underwear the army gave us were olive green slips and panties; no bras and no girdles, so we had to buy our own. For three years our supply sergeant kept telling us that WAAC bras were on order and coming. There was an amusing story making the rounds near the end of the war. It seems the army was conducting an inventory in one of its warehouses when they unearthed huge boxes, all stored in the kitchen equipment section, and labeled Cup A, Cup B, and Cup C. Just in time for the next war.

Our pay as privates was $50.00 a month. The army had pressured me into buying an $18.75 war bond each month, so my net pay amounted to $31.25. This amount had to cover toothpaste, lipstick, cigarettes, postage, silk stockings, recreation, and hopefully, train fare back home on furlough. Two weeks after payday, we were all broke. It took me two full months to gather enough courage to tell the army what they could do with the war bond.

Our training started immediately. We marched from morning to night, every place we went—even to eat. And we never marched from one place to another in a straight line. We practiced close order drill all the way; forward, backward, and sideways. We learned how to make beds and store our gear the army way. We did it over, and over, and over until we got it right. We stood inspection after inspection and ended up scrubbing the cracks in the barracks floor with toothbrushes.

We were divided into companies, and then into squads by height. I'll never know why the army puts the tallest people at the head of a column and the shortest people in the back. I ran for an entire month trying to keep up with the people in front of me. At 5:00 a.m. we fell out for reveille because it was so hot they gave us two hours off at noon. Every night we stood retreat in full uniform, pulling them on over sweaty bodies without the luxury of a shower. I never learned how to knot a necktie properly. Once tied, I just kept loosening it and pulling it over my head.

We struggled through obstacle courses and did calistenics on the parade ground. The hot sand burned through the soles of our shoes and blistered our hands as we strove to do pushups. We learned to keep our mouths shut and say, "Yes, Ma'm" and "No, Ma'm" and nothing else. Training films and lectures were my favorite form of training—I got to sit down.

When I first arrived in Florida the sudden change of climate and intense heat made me weak and I had trouble eating. That ended when I was introduced to salt tablets which stood in bowls everywhere: mess hall, barracks, and bathrooms. There was a trick to it though. If you didn't consume at least a full glass of water with each tablet, the concentration of salt in your stomach would soon come up and bring everything else along with it.

Every Saturday was shot day—typhoid, tetanus, and small pox given in a series of three for three straight weeks. We passed in long lines down the middle of a barracks between tables piled high with needles and serums. When you came abreast of a medic, he would grab your arm and ram home a needle; then you moved on to the next one, who got the opposite arm. We suffered our red swollen arms on our own time; Sunday was our day off.

When anyone dropped from heat prostration, we simply stepped over her and kept going. I marched behind a girl with blood splashing out of the back of her shoes from busted blisters. She kept on marching. I remember lying in my bunk one noon, utterly exhausted, when the whistle blew for us to fall out. The woman in the bunk next to me, who was thirty years old, struggled to her feet. All I could think of was, "If that old lady can do it, you have got to do it too."

The first time I drew K.P. duty, I was assigned to pots and pans. The army doesn't own a pot or pan smaller than a wash tub. I stood in front of a huge sink, pots and pans piled high on the floor around me. I had all I could do to lift a pot into the sink. If it slipped from my hands and dropped, I was hit with a tidal wave of greasy dishwater. The temperature outside the mess hall hovered around 100 degrees; inside with the stoves and steamers going, it was closer to 140 degrees. I hung over the huge sink, greasy hair falling in my eyes, sweat pouring from my face into the dishwater, and scrubbed and scratched and scrubbed. It seemed like the pile of pots never went down because the cooks kept adding to it. The only way I could reach the bottom of some of the pots was to hang on my belly on the sink's edge. When it was over, I slunk home, a sopping wet grease ball, and crawled into the barracks on my hands and knees.

The next time on K.P. duty, I drew the garbage cans. The army sorts its garbage into cans of edible food, bones, egg shells, and coffee grounds. After each meal, farmers would show up to haul away the edible food for pig feed, and the army hauled away the rest. It was my job to keep the garbage sorted and to wash and disinfect each can as it was dumped. I worked outside in the hot sun amid swarms of flies. The only way I could scrub the bottom of the cans was to crawl inside, then back out, and wrestle them back into line.

We also walked guard duty at night—four hours off and four hours on. Armed with a billy club and flashlight, covered with mosquito repellant, I wasn't afraid of anything that walked on two legs. I was terrified of anything that crawled. I burned out my flashlight batteries examining every twig and branch in the road looking for coral snakes.

We were given the same basic training as men except for rifle practice. We crawled on our stomachs through fields of tear gas, blinded by our masks, and learned that the gas not only chokes, but burns as well. With full packs on our backs, we marched for miles in the hot sun. My nose never got tan. It just burned bright red, peeled, and burned again. My hair bleached almost white where it wasn't covered by my fatigue hat and looked like a poor dye job trying to grow out.

Our only time off was Sunday afternoon, so we spent it lying on Daytona Beach. Even though we were dressed in the latest style of bathing suits, we were easy to spot. Our beautiful suntans reached only to the middle of our arms where our dress sleeves ended, and dog tags dangled from around our necks.

In August the army converted the corps from an auxilliary unit to regular army. From now on we would be WACs, rather than WAACs. We had a choice at this point; we could get out of the corps or re-enlist in the new army. Only one woman in our company decided to call it quits. We were not surprised. She was older than most of us and had spent every free moment on the telephone to her congressman pleading to get out.

The rest of us pinned our green WAAC ribbons above our left breast pockets and decided to hang around. The ribbon was a symbol of our service in the original WAAC. We were all lean, brown, tough and disciplined. We could pass in review with the best of troops. We had taken all the garbage the army could throw at us and survived. We had pride in ourselves and in our outfit. We were soldiers!

Ode to Boots

Vernon Carlson
Buffalo, Minnesota

Gee, Dad,
can't my new boots
have a pocket knife
on the side
instead of
a dumb
old compass?
Who needs it?
I hike, and trap,
and hunt along
the river—
not a chance of
getting lost—
of not finding
my way home.

After a snowstorm
through deep snow
on unplowed streets,
a symbol
of fortitude—
the small pool
of water under
the school desk,
melted snow from
boots not
thoroughly stomped.

Melted tallow
for waterproofing
works until
it dries out
and cracks.
Once or twice

a year,
when the teacher
isn't looking,
a booted leg
extends to
the radiator.
Soon the stink
of rancid tallow
fills the room.

Like two
muddy toads
my army boots
squat
by the tent wall.
When the mud
has dried,
I brush it off
and put on
more M-1
Boot-Waterproofing-
Compound
which doesn't
help
when the water
comes in
over the tops.

You know what
the army
should do?
They should
put
a compass
in a pocket
on the side
of the boot

so
a soldier
can find
his way
home.

excerpt from
The Land of 10,000 Hints

Mickie Scholtus
River Falls, Wisconsin

"The same thing happened on the first day of deer hunting season last year, Dad. It couldn't be just a coincidence. One of those stupid hunters killed Grey-Grey. Last year they shot Charlie on opening day. You know that as well as I do. There was so much shooting going on around here yesterday, it sounded like World War II. They shoot anything that moves. If it happens to be your pet cat, that's just too bad."

Lee was directing his grievances to Jay, who knew that Lee spoke for the family, that it would be difficult to interject effectively what little logic he could summon. Grey-Grey was a special cat, just as Charlie had been a special cat. We had cried when Charlie disappeared. If we had found him dead somewhere, it might have been easier to take, but having him simply disappear, never to know how his death came, not being there to help him, was very difficult for all of us to accept.

"Lee, we don't know for sure that our neighbors shot Grey-Grey — or Charlie for that matter." Jay knew before he spoke that his half-hearted attempt at logic would be overruled.

"Sure, Dad," said Paul. "A hawk picked up Charlie on the first day of deer hunting season last year, and yesterday he came back and picked up Grey-Grey. Maybe we should try to get this into the *Guiness Book of World Records*. How does this sound: In two consecutive years, 1974 and 1975, on the first day of deer hunting season in Morgan Township, Minnesota, a hawk swooped down, picked up a cat, and carried him away. Both cats belonged to the same family. Could it possibly have been the same hawk each time?"

"Here comes a battalion of hunters," warned Marc pointing south from our dining room window, interrupting any comments that might have been made on Paul's suggestion. Marc, whom we had adopted at the age of four in 1967 and who had never let the fact that he was the youngest child get in the way of his developing a strong position in the family unit, was ready to protect our privacy and commitment. "Don't they know they're not supposed to hunt on our land, Dad?" Marc added.

We all looked to see who it was and how many. Coming across the corn stubble to the southwest of our house were nine men dressed in hunting gear all of the same red hue — pink-red, ugly and out of place in the gorgeous bright fall morning. I might have settled for that anemic red had I known that in a few more years the hunters would appear in garish, flourescent orange outfits that stood out like neon signs in broad daylight. Coming upon a group of hunters wearing their guns and their shiny colors of hell and purgatory was intimidating. These men were in their weekend uniform and had the ammunition and numbers to pack up more than threats to deer.

"They're all related," said Paul.

"No, they're not," said Lee. "It just looks that way because three or four of them are related. Three or four of them are on the road maintenance crew, too, but when they get together and walk across your land like this, it looks like Power, Incorporated."

With the impetuousness of a twelve-year-old, Marc announced that he was going to confront the hunters "right now." "I'll tell them that they can't shoot deer on our property, and I'll ask them which one killed Grey-Grey. Will you go with me, Dad?"

"Sure," Jay answered, "but let me do the talking."

I opened the window a bit so I could hear the conversation, knowing it would be like all the conversations we had had with these men for the last decade. Unfriendly. Lots of priming on our part to produce a trickle of response.

"I'm sorry," I heard Jay say, "but you know that we don't allow the shooting of deer on our land — or any other wild game for that matter. Our land is a wildlife refuge."

"Deer have to be harvested," said one of the men.

"I realize that," said Jay, "and they are being harvested in a big way outside our 160 acres."

"We just want to walk across to where we can shoot," said another man.

"No," replied Jay. "Not with guns. When you are out of sight I have no way of knowing who is shooting where. I said O.K.

to that once before, but I have done some re-thinking about it. We see these deer everyday. They are our animal friends and..." he was interrupted by macho laughter, but he persisted, "and we protect them. One year we gave in and let you hunt. You drove past our window that night with a deer you had killed draped over the roof of your truck, and it made us sick thinking it might have been the doe we watched nursing her twins during the summer months. We just don't like it."

"It's unfair. You are the only neighbor making a bottle neck," protested one of the men, completely ignoring Jay's explanation.

"Which one of you shot our cats?" demanded Marc. There was a long silence while we all waited for some kind of reply. Finally, we heard one of them laugh and say, "You should keep your cats inside during hunting season."

"We do!" shouted Marc. "And we keep our dogs in too. But they have to go outside to go to the bathroom!"

Knowing Jay was not about to change his mind, the hunters turned around to double back. In exchanges loud enough for us to hear, they let us know that they considered us "weird" and "poor neighbors." One of them hung back a bit because he wanted to yell one last insult at us. "Thanks for making a federal case out of it!" That the nine of them had ignored our "No Trespassing" and "No Hunting" signs, as well as our long-standing policy of using our land as a game refuge, and, armed with rifles, had brazenly marched up to our house seemed to mean nothing to them. In their eyes we were uncooperative culprits making a "case" out of their breaking the law. What they planned to do to have their way for the rest of the hunting season we could only surmise. They did the planning where we could neither hear nor see them. We were given only a few hints now and then by someone who thought it best we should know.

One of these "someones" was our closest neighbor, George. He had a select list of gripes against these same people, and that, I believe, formed the basis of our friendship, that and the fact that we spoke up when the situation called for it. He admired anyone who spoke up.

Unfortunately, our friendship was not an outgrowth of our

having been on the same frequency on pertinent issues; he was as much opposed, for instance, to keeping the BWCA in wilderness status as were the majority of the Iron Range residents. Our stance against the United States' involvement in Viet Nam puzzled him, although he didn't go so far as to label us Communists for having an opinion, as did a lot of other people.

George had been born and reared on the Range. He knew the people well, and he kept his eyes and ears open for the trouble he knew lurked behind every snow bank. Feeling protective toward us, his vigilance carried over naturally into our lives.

Knowing his ability to find trouble whether it existed or not, I was inclined to ignore his warnings the day he told us that the maintenance crew was plotting to "get even" with us. George did not say why they were getting even. Although our family had tried to prevent an unhealthy relationship from forming, from the beginning it had been us against them. The lines had been formed long before our arrival. It was like being a black person living among red-necks in the south. In the case of the blacks, their crime was the color of their skin. In our case, it was the philosophies by which we lived.

George was right. It seems that when the access road to his and our property was built in the 1930's, it had been necessary to make a jog that terminated the access just before it reached the land that was to become ours. A short, curved stretch of land that linked the access to our turnaround then became, legally, private, and the township was not obligated to maintain that tiny portion. Apparently, reason had prevailed, and the plowing and grading of the jog and the turnaround had always been done as a matter of course. Now, the head of the road crew had resurrected this technicality, planning to use it as a basis for discontinuing our service.

Jay went to the Town Board to protest the scheme. The sympathetic Board Chair ordered the crew to continue servicing our road, but we noticed that during the summer months the grading stopped at our land, suggesting (hinting) that it was to be abandoned, a decision which could have been an inconvenience during the summer months, but one that could be absolutely life-threatening during the winter.

Another protest to the Town Board proved fruitful. The

Board's attorney ruled that because the township had been maintaining the road in its entirety for some thirty years, it had no legal right suddenly to stop doing so.

After that, the crew plowed, but did so haphazardly. No longer trying to elicit any explanations from the crew members, once again Jay went to the Township Board. Here we learned that suddenly our road had become difficult to plow because the snow could be thrown only one way, and the tree limbs posed damage to the lights on the top of the grader. It was hinted that if two magnificent pines were to be cut down, plowing would be resumed.

Until this time, no one had ever hinted that our trees presented maintenance problems. Had just one person communicated that difficulty, we would have cut off the offending limbs without hesitation. We will never know whether the limbs' extensions had anything to do with the decision to discontinue maintenance. I found it difficult to accept the complaint as a bona fide one because for three decades the turnaround had always been cleared, the trees' positions notwithstanding. Surely, had the trees been a major handicap, we would have noticed, or something would have been said.

A few days later the crew's boss came out to see us. After trying to convince Jay that we should cut down our trees, he grudgingly settled for a promise of some limb trimming, marking off the limbs in questions. While Jay and the boss talked, I looked at our trees, wondering how anyone could suggest we cut them down.

The Pro

Albert McClure
Minneapolis, Minnesota

I'm sitting on the training table in my dressing room, legs dangling, one arm outstretched as my trainer starts carefully bandaging my hand. I'm nervous; my back and shoulder muscles are tense; a light sweat covers my body. I've got to calm down and relax.

"Make a fist! Does it feel O.K.? Spread your fingers—bandage too tight? No? Good."

I'm beginning to relax. I look around—all fighters's dressing rooms look the same—grubby lockers and shower at one end, a bench and two rickety chairs at the other. And they all smell—the familiar stench of liniment, rubbing alchohol and stale sweat.

I think about the fighters who have waited in this room—some on the way up, others on the way down, and some who'd end up punch-drunk. Not me, me and Johnny D, my trainer-manager. We're too smart for that.

I stare at the balding head of Johnny D, intent in his work, and I feel a wave of affection for this battle-scarred ex-pug. Beneath the scar tissue, concerned brown eyes look up at me. He knows the pitfalls, the danger of our profession. His devotion and dedication have made me the complete polished fighter. I owe him! I watch him fuss over me like a mother hen.

Johnny D's sharp, "Let's put on the gloves; time to warm up," brings me back to the business at hand. "Can't enter the ring cold you know. "Ten minutes later he says, "Ease up, baby." Then raising his opened right hand as a target, he mumbles, "Snap it baby, with a left jab. 1-2-3-4 that's it, baby. Remember, he might slip the first jab but not the second or third in a row. Jab! Jab! Jab! Now hook off the jab!" His face lights up—excitement starts creeping into his voice. "That's it baby! Jab, jab—hook! Now a combination L-R-L and a double hook."

I hear a faint roar outside; the fight crowd sounds bloodthristy. There's a knock at the door and a muffled voice shouts, "Hey, you're on."

Johnny D drapes a towel over my head, slips my robe over my sweating body, gives me a hard hug. He's smiling now. "Come on, boy, time to see if you've learned anything. Let's show them a real fighter." The adrenalin starts flowing.

We enter the underground tunnel. Ahead I see the brightly lit ring; I hear the catcalls of aroused fight fans. Surrounded by my trainer and corner men, I enter the arena. At the sight of me, the crowd goes wild — a roar shakes the rafters, the butterflies in my stomach disappear — this is what I've trained so hard for — this is what I want. I am a fighter! Caught up in excitement, I climb up into the ring.

There's another roar as my opponent, Benito Hernandez, enters the ring. I keep dancing up and down in my corner, anxious to get started. I listen to the introductions. The referee calls us to the center of the ring. I barely listen to familiar instructions . . . no hitting on the break . . . no kidney punches . . . penality for low blow . . . in case of a knockdown, go to the farthest neutral corner and remain there 'til I tell you to come out . . . protect yourself at all times . . . shake hands . . . good luck.

Hernandez keeps trying to psyche me, stare me down. I look him over. Seems strong. What about hand speed — that could cause me trouble. I look at the scar tissue above his eyes, especially his left eye; looks a little puffy — a catcher? We'll soon see if I'm right. Mentally, I'm checking for possible flaws. I glance down at his midriff; seems a little flabby — check it out. He's still trying to outstare me. Psyche is not my game; brains and power is my name.

I go back to my corner, Johnny D inserts my mouthpiece, smears more vaseline over my face, especially around my eyes and cheekbones. I turn and face Hernandez. "Remember, box him this round, get the feel, then go get him," whispers Johnny D. The bell rings. Round one.

Hernandez comes out with a rush. I circle him, jabbing with my left 1-2-3-4 (light taps). He swings a wild right and left. I back away. He follows close. We clinch. He tries to bull me inside; he also tries to butt me. I move my head away from danger and tie him up. I start boxing again. He comes at me with a flurry of hard punches. Some punches land on my arms, my shoulders. I can feel their power. An overhand right catches me high on my head. It hurts me. I cover up. Careful, he's dangerous. I start boxing. Jab-jab-hook – a right cross – each time harder. I set him up for a right hand – solid – on the button. He seemed surprised at its power. Ba-ay-bee, you ain't seen nothing yet. I'm starting to get into the rythmic flow of the fight, moving from side to side, popping him. Like I said, he's a catcher.

In my corner, Johnny D says, "OK, kid. Nice work. Don't slug with him. Now go downstairs, but keep him worried about his head. Work him good." The bell rings. Round two.

I go to work. I'm moving flat-footed now, my punches more crisp, more powerful. He's coming straight at me, bobbing up and down, and my fists keep finding his face like homing pigeons. Thud! Thud! I keep popping him. His hands come up to protect his face. I feint at his head, then throw a hard left hook under his arm to the body. I feel him sag as the blow goes home; he grabs me and hangs on. I start working, smashing body blows, softening him up. I get in two solid uppercuts before the referee separates us. He's breathing heavy now. His face is swelling; his left eye is starting to close; blood trickles from his nose. I go after him, sensing I can finish him, but he gamely hangs on until the round ends.

Before the start of round three, the referee carefully looks Hernandez over and signals for the fight to continue. At the bell, Hernandez rushes at me, swinging wild desperation punches. I set him up with a hard left jab followed by a crushing right hand to his jaw. His head snaps back, his mouthpiece flies out, and he sags into the ropes. Quickly I follow, hitting him a series of left and righthand smashes to the head before the referee steps between us, grabs him, and waves me away. I still want to go after him; a feeling of power engulfs me. I'm invincible! I come back to reality as the referee raises my hand in victory. Over the P.A. system I hear the ring announcer: "La-ay-dees and Gen-n-n-tel-men-n-n . . . THE WIN-NAH by a TKO . . . 24 seconds of the third round, John (THE DE-STROYER) Bible!"

NO REGRETS:
SHAPES OF LOVE

No Regrets

Lowell E. Haas
Deerwood, Minnesota

W ell, at least one of my ideas came out like I figured. I always told Ada, the only way a man could provide for his keep when he got old was to have lots of kids. Best old age insurance possible, I told her. Funny how when you are on the borrowed-time side of seventy, it is so easy to remember the things of forty and fifty years ago. All my big plans. All the while I was telling Ada how the kids would take care of whichever one was left, I didn't believe they would have to do it. What happened to that insurance company do you suppose? Ha! Don't have to wonder what happened to the old Citizen's National Bank; it went broke. No sir! Forty years ago I would have laughed at any man who said I would be living at my daughter's house when I was seventy-two but, by golly, here I am.

They make it easy for me though. Fixed this big upstairs room for me. They even built a little kitchen in what used to be the clothes closet. If I get to feeling in the way, I don't have to bother them at all. I have a little radio. And they bought me a new-fangled machine to give me my own private movies, only when I tune the thing in, it looks like the people are walking around in spaghetti soup.

I wonder if I am talking out loud? My thoughts get so sharp I wouldn't be surprised if I did. Living up here reminds me of the first year Ada and I were married. We were married in a Quaker Meeting House. We didn't have a real Quaker wedding though, where you say your own vows when the Spirit moves you. No, we fixed it with John Thomas to call us up and to read a short ceremony after the regular Sunday worship service was finished. When he was through, I said, "I Adam take thee Ada to be my wife," and she returned the promise with, "I Ada take thee Adam to be my husband." It worked out just fine too. The kids think it's terrible that I don't mourn any more than I do for Ada. We knew all through the years that the one left wouldn't have any regrets. It's a little over a year now since she died.

We had fun that first year. We lived in an upstairs apartment just like I'm doing now. The apartment wasn't all together though. It was in a house, owned by an old man named Wills, in one of those suburban towns north of Chicago. When you entered the front door, the stairway was directly in front. The telephone was on a little table just to the left of the stairs. Halfway up the stairs was a landing where you turned sharp left to continue on up. The first door on the left led into the housekeeper's room. That bed of hers! I know I'm laughing out loud now. I just don't want to get into an old man's habit of talking out loud. That bed of the housekeeper's. It had blocks a foot high under each leg at the foot. She told Ada that during the day her blood all collected in her feet and got stagnant, so she had her bed tipped so that it would run back up at night.

The door directly ahead of the stairs went into our parlor-bedroom. It was a long, pleasant room just right for us then. Next door to the right was Mr. Wills' bedroom. He was as old then as I am now. He wasn't nearly as lucky though. He lost his wife fifteen years before he was seventy-two while I only lost mine a little while ago. He had cancer, too, while I'm still whole as far as I know. Following on around the hall, the next door on the left opened on our kitchen-dining room, and the one on the right was for the bathroom.

Oh, we had fun that first year. We played tricks on each other. Once I fixed the tooth powder can with toilet paper so that tooth powder couldn't come out but flour would. Ada brushed her teeth three times before she asked me if I didn't think the tooth powder was gluey. She got back at me though; she tricked me into thinking that she was in the bathroom while it was really the housekeeper. I'll bet I'm blushing now again.

Mr. Wills and his housekeeper were good to us, most of the time, that is. Once they made Ada cry. They told her she could use the washing machine in the basement. It was an old one, but I guess they thought it was an extra good one. She left it running once while she ran up to our room to get some more clothes. When she came back Mr. Wills really lectured her. Told her she couldn't use it any more if she went off and let it run; what if it broke while she was upstairs; might tear it all to pieces. I suppose the old goat thought it would go to powder or something. Now I'm an old goat. They liked us all right though. Mr.

Wills let me drive his Franklin car once when it was raining and I had to take someone to the train. The housekeeper told Ada he had never let anyone drive it in all the years she had worked for the Wills.

Now I am thinking about the ghost. We never doubted, then, that there might not be a ghost. There couldn't have been one though, not really. It must just have been that old house creaking. The ghost seemed real that first year though. We were sitting in our parlor-bedroom with the door closed when we heard Mr. Wills come upstairs and go into his bedroom. We kept reading or whatever it was we were doing—it probably wasn't reading that first year—when the stairs began to creak and footsteps came up again. Ada shushed me until the housekeeper could get into her room. Those footsteps didn't go into the first door on the left though; they crossed the hall and went into Mr. Wills' room. I remember how our eyes said, "Aha." After we talked about it, though, we couldn't see anything so bad in it. After all, fifteen years is a long time to live in a house with a widower and just be the housekeeper.

Seems simple, doesn't it? The trouble was, a couple of weeks later we were in our room again when footsteps followed Mr. Wills upstairs and crossed the hall when they should have turned left. After a few minutes, when we were unfolding our studio bed, the phone rang in the hall below. We were wondering whether we should go answer it or not when the housekeeper called, "Ada, it's for you." Our eyes locked. If she's downstairs, who followed him upstairs?

I wonder how you trap a ghost? We tried to trap that one. We studied the way Mr. Wills came up the stairs. We listened to how the housekeeper's steps sounded. We became certain that there was a third set of footsteps that used the stairs and followed Mr. Wills into his room. We opened the door quickly when the steps came to the top landing. The hall was always empty. We dusted talcum powder, ever so lightly, in the hall; male footprints went into Mr. Wills' room, female ones went into the housekeeper's, but no female ones ever showed following Mr. Wills.

Neither of us was ever afraid to be alone up there. I suppose that was because we laughed and said, "Mrs. Wills is with him tonight," or "Here comes Mrs. Wills." It couldn't have been her though. It must have just been that old house creaking. Just like this one is doing now. All the folks below have gone visiting while I'm up here thinking, thinking, thinking. These stairs are creaking now as if someone about Ada's size was climbing them. That's strange. There *are* footsteps coming to my room. I'd better open the door. Oh, ho, ho! No need, if it's her.

The Dream

Albert McClure
Minneapolis, Minnesota

I am a condor soaring high above the Andes. Far below, a rabbit moves across the rocky terrain. I hover, motionless, a black dot in the bright blue sky. I bank, then hurtle downward, falling in a graceful arc toward my unsuspecting prey. I strike and carry it to my nest.

I am eating a chocolate. Before me are lots of chocolates—sweet exotic chocolates—large and small ones with strawberry and brandy creme centers. I hunger. I lust and I gorge myself!

On a smooth white beach lies a giant striated mollusk. I open it. Embedded in the clam is a magnificent black pearl, breathtaking in its beauty. I must caress it! The dream fades...

I awake. Sleepily I turn and touch you. *You* are the hare, the feast of chocolate, the magnificent black pearl of my dream.

a chapter from
The Coif and the Crown
Norah O'Leary Sorem
Minneapolis, Minnesota

D onna Lapa slammed shut the garden gate with the violence that betrays an urge to break something. She was
panting, but couldn't decide if it was due to her rapid descent
of the hill behind her, crowned with the austere monastery of
San Domenico, or to the fury that soured and burned inside her,
stirring up the digestive misery she had been experiencing the
past ten days.

She stared sullenly at the rear door of her house, thinking of
the difficult stairs in a dwelling built into the side of a hill, with
the kitchen on the upper level, the loft above that. Already her
legs felt tired.

Last evening, Lapa's fiery temper had again scorched her
dear, patient Jacopo, and this morning she felt contrite enough
to walk the steep hill to San Domenico and make confession to
one of the friars, hoping that would put her in a better mood for
mass in the morning. But the familiar routine had provided neither a catharsis nor the longed-for benediction. She could still
hear that monotonous, flat voice: "My daugther, to be angry—
or even to feel despondent—because you again carry life in your
womb is sinful rebellion against God's will. Remember Saint
Monica, who also suffered the burden of Eve's sin. Pray to her
for patience."

"Saint Monica suffered, too," muttered Lapa with clenched
teeth. "Saint Monica suffered—what does that whey faced
priest know about women's suffering?" She jerked off the shawl
that covered her hair and tossed her head with a defiance she
could not show the Dominican.

Despite her rage, as she hastened toward the house her
proprietory eye took inventory of the small garden: a half-
cupful of beans left on the dried stalks must be harvested at
once; grandchildren had been romping too close to the rose
bush and had broken off a branch; small footprints indicated

that Stefano had just run across the herb garden—well, it was impossible for the darling *bambino* to remember all the rules.

Any reminder of her beautiful son could soften Lapa. But on this day it was only another fagot on the fire of her anger. Stefano was now three years old. She had been sure that he was her final baby, to cherish and enjoy the most, a symbol of the conclusion of nearly three decades of reproductive duty.

Bustling into the kitchen, she tossed her shawl over the rod behind the door and turned to see Tonetta, the maidservant, hastily wiping up spilled buttermilk. The mistress seized a heavy skillet to bang for emphasis while she scolded—and at this unfortunate moment Jacopo Benincasa came up the stairs at the far end of the kitchen.

The sight of him reminded Lapa that in her distress she had forgotten to tell Tonetta to prepare a traveler's lunch for Betto, the elder journeyman, who was probably now waiting to sling it over the neck of the mule Jacopo always borrowed from neighbor Bernardo whenever someone made a business trip thirty miles north to Florence.

Defensiveness fired her rage to a higher pitch. Lapa hurled the skillet at her husband. The aim, however, was as uncoordinated as her thoughts, and the iron pan sped past his head and through the open doorway to bounce noisily down the stairwell. Jacopo went rigid with astonishment. He was accustomed to his wife's tongue-lashings but not this, for no violence was permitted in the Benincasa family.

"Congratulations," she screamed. "You can once again strut in front of the other bulls on the *campo* when they stand around to stare at the women doing their marketing."

Jacopo's face, which had paled when she hurled the skillet, changed to the scarlet flush that was all he ever showed of anger, even when disciplining one of his numerous household. Lapa, as well as his sons and their children, knew that neither violent tantrums nor vulgarity was allowed under the roof of this pious house.

"Mama, you know that is not my custom."

"But it certainly is your custom to put more shove into night-work than any other man in Siena." She placed her hands on her hips and contemptuously turned her back. Jacopo moved toward her cautiously.

Tonetta saw her chance to dart from the kitchen and race down the stairs, stumbling at the bottom to fall against Betto, who was standing in the open doorway, occupied with holding the reins in one hand and the flung skillet in the other. The collision of their bodies made the mule shy, and all stirred up the dust of the narrow street. Betto could not stop laughing at the sound and fury of the drama above, carried down the stairs by Lapa's loud voice.

"Well, where's my lunch?"

'What are you talking about?" Tonetta snapped, as she sat down on the bottom step to rub a twisted ankle. "You should thank God that you take your orders from the master instead of from her."

"And he ordered me to start as soon as I could fetch the mule." Betto handed the reins to a small boy who had come running to enjoy the commotion and reached out an arm to help the girl to her feet – glad of an excuse to squeeze her waist and feel a woman's arm around his neck.

"I don't think we should go up until they have finished fighting."

"Oh, I don't mind listening. It will be a good reminder not to get married."

"And it will remind me not to get a baby from you." As she struggled to free herself, he nipped her ear. She blushed, then decided to gasp as if in pain, and let him help her – slowly – up the steep stairs, while they both listened.

Lapa was giving her husband the tongue-lashing she had not dared to lay on the friar. "What has Saint Monica to do with me? Tell me that, man, tell me! Monica had one precious son to worry about – the other gave her no trouble at all. How many sons have I had to look after? Count them, man. Monica's husband was rich enough to pamper their clever Augustine and to give his wife many servants. And how many servants have I? Monica's son became a saint. Ha!" She clasped her hands and rolled her eyes heavenward in mock piety. "Am I likely to become the mother of saint, too. But will anyone ever praise me for producing this baby?" She thumped her belly and glared at him.

"I will love you for it, Lapa, and praise you, too." His dark eyes pleaded. He opened his arms.

The wife looked at him for a moment while the anger drained away. There was just enough strength left in her to rush to him and sob with her head on his shoulder.

Anna

Gladys I. Pearson
Bemidji, Minnesota

T he first time I saw her, I was down on my hands and knees scrubbing the back steps of the house we'd purchased a few days before. I was unaware of her presence until she spoke.

"Well, it's good to see you like clean steps. Always did say you could tell an awful lot about people living in a house by the appearance of the doorway."

There she stood—tall, angular, strength in every muscle and in her voice as well. Her gray hair was pinned back, and her faded print dress was clean. On her feet she wore a pair of frayed tennis shoes over men's black socks.

She introduced herself, then, as my next door neighbor. I invited her in, and she rapidly gave me a rundown on all the things we'd find wrong with the house as well as the many intricacies of the neighborhood. She advised me to keep my door locked as there were no less than two dozen children within the block who would take over if allowed to do so. I took the advice with a grain of salt.

She told me she was a baby-sitter, which certainly sounded inviting. Yet I wondered about the stern lines in her face, the sharpness of her speech, her brusque manner. Would my children like her? And what was more important, would she like them?

After she left, I looked out our bedroom window which faced Anna's house. It was a basement house built high enough so that there were many windows above the ground level. Her doorstep was clean and neat, as was her yard and garden. Somehow, I knew it would be to my advantage to be in the good graces of this woman.

As time went on, I learned many things about Anna. Always she presented a hard exterior, but some of the things she did belied what lay on the inside. She loved to cook and bake, and often she'd leave cookies or bread on my counter without saying a word. Her house was scrupulously neat and always looked as if no one lived in it. She had many growing plants which thrived under her care. Not only that, but they always seemed perfectly formed – like a fern having the same number of fronds on each side.

Anna had a husband whose name was Hans. Hans had grown up in Norway and had been a shoemaker all his life. To Anna, Hans was a nonentity, and she treated him as such. They argued a lot, and it was apparent that no love was lost between them. In spring, when it was time to get their garden ready for seeding, Anna would get the small plow out of the shed, and harness Hans to the front of it, while she pushed at the back. I'm sure no beast ever had a more stern taskmaster. Anna planted the garden, took care of it, and gathered the produce. Hans would just make a mess of things, she said. Yet, to us, he seemed a quiet, friendly man. When he was eighty, the neighborhood decided to bake a cake and have a party. Anna gave her grudging consent. Hans said it was the first time he'd ever had a birthday cake. Anna told me later that Hans was pretty lucky to have her to care for him. She could have thrown him out, she said, after she found out he was seeking companionship elsewhere.

The day arrived, a few months later, when I needed a babysitter, so I decided to risk it with Anna. It was winter and she came wearing an ancient fur coat. Before I left, the fur coat had become a bear, and she and the children were having a most exciting time. The children loved her. Many times my two-year-old son would knock at her window when he was outdoors. Always, she'd come up the stairway with a stick of gum or a cookie. Sometimes she'd get Hans out of his chair to give my son a ride in the stroller or wagon.

As the years went by, I grew to depend on the kindness of Anna. She continued to care for my children when needed. When I was ill she brought in food and took all my ironing home and brought it back perfectly done.

Anna never changed. When Hans died she didn't cry. When it came time to sell her home and move to an apartment uptown, she never admitted that it bothered her. I missed her after she moved though I'd visit her as often as I could. She was always courteous and friendly, but I never once heard her say she was lonely or in need of help.

One day a neighbor found her lying on the floor of her apartment totally helpless. She was taken to the hospital where it was determined she had suffered a stroke. She knew no one after that. She never had to admit that she was anything but totally self-sufficient.

Rube Bartley and the Devil's Hound

Leah S. Haas
Deerwood, Minnesota

In order to tell this story, which is a favorite of children in the family, I will first have to introduce my mother's mother, Catherine Bartley. She was the only girl in her family, but she had four brothers. I have a picture of them as old men, and they were very handsome. Three had white, walrus mustaches. The Bartley boys; they were Nelse, Lem, Ed and Rube. According to the stories they had the reputation of being hellers, especially as young men.

When their sister Kate married the first time, at age sixteen, to a man in his fifties, the brothers had no choice but to see her leave home with the Scotsman. After a few years had gone by, they received a pitiful letter saying that Kate had lost two children from diptheria and two more, Ella and Will, had been born. The letter also told of the abuse she took from McLean, and that he would not allow her to leave.

Lem Bartley picked up his gun, saddled his horse and rode out to rescue his sister Kate. When he arrived in Monticello, McLean was watching for him and ordered him off his place. They met on a little foot bridge that crossed a stream in front of the house and shot it out. It sounds a bit wild west, but Lem proved to be the better shot, and Kate picked up her kids and rode away with her brother. I don't know who picked up the wounded McLean.

Kate soon found it was difficult to get work and keep her children, so she placed little Ella and Will in an orphanage and went to work as a housekeeper for a widower with seven children. Quite a few months went by before old Grandma Bartley heard that her grandchildren had been left in an orphanage. Bless her heart, she hitched up the buggy and drove to Decatur and brought them home. Since her own grown sons often gathered at her house to play cards, drink and fight, Grandma Bartley probably didn't notice the noise of a couple of small kids. She greased the children's hair with goose fat to keep the head lice away, fed them clabbered milk with sugar on it, and sent them to school. Living among the uncles often brought excitement to Ella's and Will's young lives, like the time when they watched Nelse and Ed fighting in a hay mow and Nelse fell out of the high door and broke his leg.

Also there was the time . . . well, it started this way. Rube had gone to town to buy new boots, but before the afternoon was over he met some of his cronies at the tavern, so it was late at night by the time he felt hunger pangs and decided to head home. The sky was mostly overcast, the moon alternating with clouds, and a hint of ground fog lay in the low places along the road. He walked slowly, looking at his new boots and not thinking of anything in particular. As he neared a Y in the road, he suddenly noticed something large and dark at the edge of the woods on the right side of the fork. Being a cautious man, he stepped into the roadside brush and cut a heavy staff. When he hesitantly drew nearer, it looked somewhat like a huge dog sitting on its haunches. As he was nearly even with it, the cloud moved off the moon and he saw that it was indeed a dog about five feet high to the shoulders, and worst of all, it had no head. Rube took off in the direction of the house. In spite of his new boots, he covered the last two miles so fast that, no doubt, he set a world's record.

Rube was completely sober and white as a sheet when he fell through the kitchen door, gasping for breath. It was some minutes before he stopped shaking and panting and could talk about his frightful experience. Some people did not believe his story, and others thought it was a trick of his mind brought on by the life he had led. Nonetheless, Rube knew what he had seen, and never again would he walk to town. From then on he rode his horse at full gallop past the fork in the road.

Red Shoes at Sixty

Helen Earle Simcox
Mankato, Minnesota

She dons red shoes
and is small again,
going to her first party.

Too poor—
too practical
all these years for
anything but neutral
go-with-everything hues,
she hankered secretly
for the heartening
magic of red.

She's like a garden
staging a grand finale
before the curtain
of winter falls—
one last fling,
one flaunting of
brave color
before the snow.

Polka Dot Years
excerpts from a journal
Phyllis J. Peterson
Minneapolis, Minnesota

December 1, 1986

H ere she comes again; she's wearing a navy blue and white
polka dot dress just as she did three years ago when I first
began volunteering at this Loaves and Fishes meal site. However, the polka dot dress that she wore for two and a half years,
and which hung in threads around her thighs, has now been
replaced by a somewhat newer version of the same model.

Why would someone replace a disintegrated garment with
another practically identical in style and color? This is only one
of a myriad of questions I have about this person who, when I
first greeted her three years ago, cowered like a frightened animal and backed across the room. A woman in her thirties, graceful, refined and, in spite of needing dental care, strikingly beautiful. Shoulder length dark blond hair, highlighted by a few
frosted strands; round cerulean eyes which reveal about as
much pain as I can bear to see at one time. Erratic black eye liner
and a furrowed brow accent an agony which needs no underlin-
ing. Each eye is an exclamation point of pathos. Is she being
physically abused? Has she been in a mental institution? Does
she live on the streets?

She wears a pair of split-apart, ankle-high shoes, dark cotton
lisle hose with runs up the backs, a maroon cardigan sweater,
and a lime green corduroy jacket in spring and fall, a light blue,
full length corduroy coat with hood in winter. I believe she has
two rayon scarves, her only change in dress.

Any attempts at minimal conversation with her die at initial
overture. She prefers to eat in silence, looking only at her plate
or cup, carefully daubing her mouth with a paper napkin after
three or four bites. I am reminded of the book title *You Can't Push
the River* when I sit across from her.

Why do I continue trying to connect with her? There are
plenty of guests dining on Monday evenings—nearly five hun-

dred at the end of every month when welfare checks run out. As a hospitality person, I talk with many of them; some have become real buddies. Harvey and Lois tell nostalgic, often humorous tales of Cedar Rapids, Iowa; Jeannie confides she was nearly raped behind the 7-11 store last Saturday night; Harold reminisces about growing up near the River Road and Lake Street in the forties. But between visits with these persons, between carrying plates to the tables for small children or locating a booster chair for a toddler, I am pulled toward the lady in the polka dot dress. I have a need to link with her. Is that selfish on my part? She's here for a hot meal and that's all. Or is it? In three years her total staccato responses can be counted on one hand.

I watch as she sets her plastic plate of macaroni and cheese, peas and carrots, half an orange, and two slices of buttered white bread on the masonite table. Her chocolate cupcake is placed to the upper left of her plate. Carefully she unwraps her white plastic fork and spoon from a white paper napkin and positions them just as a waiter would do a La Tortue. She catches the eye of the beverage server and with a scarcely audible voice requests the usual, a styrofoam cup of milk.

After a few moments I walk slowly to her table and risk sitting down across from her. Minutes go by as we eat. Finally I swallow hard and ask, "Is there anything you need or want?" She lifts her eyes and looks into mine, riveting me there for twenty or thirty seconds. This woman who has so skillfully evaded my glance for years suddenly freezes her pupils into my soul. I can barely keep eye contact. I am absorbing such intense pain that I don't know how much longer I can hang on. Yet I do not dare let go because I fear that I will lose her forever.

When I reach a point where I can endure no longer, she frees me. Her eyes lower. I breathe the breath of a drowning woman.

"I can't answer you right now," she says "but it is such a good question."

Don't blow this I mutter within. Don't respond. Eat. Think. After several moments I mumble, "Thank you for considering the question."

I stand, leave the building and drive home. I feel as though I have just given birth, but to what I don't know.

December 8, 1986

I am not going to Holy Rosary this evening. I'm still wiped out from last week.

December 15, 1986

I'm ready. It's the middle of the month and at least a hundred people are already in line at the site when I arrive. I join the tail end and talk with Len about his custodial work at one of the bars on Highway 7. After receiving my plate of chow mein, rice, carrot sticks, buttered bread, and cookies, I sit down across from a thirteen-year-old wearing immense multi-colored mobile earrings suspended from two holes in each of her ears. My eyes scan the tables in the church basement, then the line.

There she is . . . in her uniform. Would I recognize her in anything else? After about ten minutes she receives her food and sits down two tables away. I breathe deeply, finish my dinner, and dispose of my plate. I'll join her for coffee. That seems lighthearted, not like having dinner together. I slide into the seat across from her and say hello. She totally ignores me. It would be easier being a neuro-surgeon approaching an ill patient. All I would have to say is, "You have a massive malignant tumor in your frontal lobe." I would even know the patient's name.

After five minutes of sipping coffee I ask, "Have you thought any more about my question of a couple of weeks ago?" Directed to a close friend, the question would be too vague, but to this woman I knew it would be clear.

Silence. After an interminable length of time she says, "Yes."

Again, silence. God . . . at this rate I'll know the first letter of her middle name by 1989.

"Could you tell me if you've thought of something you want or need?"

"Yes."

Nothing more. Simply yes. Why am I here, anyway? Am I actually masochistic? I could be Christmas shopping or sticking pins into my eyeballs. I wonder if I need therapy.

108

Minutes elapse. I look up. She, too, looks up and meets me halfway across the table.

"Chocolate."

"Chocolate?"

"Yes. Chocolate."

Good heavens. My need has been for her to say a navy blue sweater or a woolen scarf or high warm boots. But chocolate? Doesn't she know that is very low on my priority list for her?

"You mean, like filled chocolates in a box?"

"No."

Silence. Am I being tested? "Like a chocolate bar?"

"No."

This time I know there will be silence, so I simply wait it out. I'm a slow learner, but I do eventually learn.

"Chocolate with caramel and peanuts," she says with firmness and succinctness. "I don't come here every night, so I don't know if you'll find me."

"I come here nearly every Monday evening," I reply, "and I'll find you."

"I have a wish, too," I say as I lower my eyes and remain very still.

Finally, I say, barely audibly, "I would like to know your first name."

"Oh, no," she says quickly as her eyes dart nervously; "oh, NO. I'm not ready for that."

"It's OK. Really, it's OK. It's not a need . . . only a wish."

Nettie Remembers

Violet M. Backe
Minnetonka, Minnesota

I hate snakes! I'm afraid of 'em too. Seems like there's always been snakes wherever I lived. When I was little in Nebraska, South Dakota and Wyoming we always had to look for snakes. There in Montana too.

My husband Guy and I lived on our Whistle Creek ranch in Montana for the first five years after we were married, before we built our house in town. We had a couple cows, some pigs and chickens, and I had a big garden. My first baby, Violet, was just two and with the cooking and cleaning there was always lots to do. Guy worked at the depot in town so he was gone all day.

I'd let Violet play by the kitchen step in the sandy dirt. I'd give her a little tin pail and a spoon to play with. It kept her quiet while I was busy working in the kitchen, and I could keep an eye on her.

One afternoon while she was taking a nap I hurried out to the spring house to get some butter, milk and eggs to bake a cake. I got my things and started back up the path toward the house when what did I see but a big old diamondback rattlesnake sunning himself by the back step—right where Violet had been playing a couple hours before. I gasped and stood stock still. I couldn't move. "What if Violet had been there when that rattler came along? What if he'd struck her little hand with his poison fangs while she was scraping dirt into her tin bucket?" I took a deep breath and moved—fast! I ran around the house, went in the front door, dumped the cake things on a chair, grabbed the gun and ran back around the house. I took aim and fired. I hit that rattler, but he crawled off under the house.

Next morning when I went out to work in the garden, there he was dragging along, his skin almost shot in two. I took the hoe and went after him. Every time I hit that snake I screamed. When I'd finished him off, I heard someone call out, "Did you get him, Mrs. Lamb?" It was the neighbor from the next ranch riding by on horseback. I didn't know there was anyone around for miles. I was so embarassed I nearly died. Believe me, I never let Violet play by that back step again.

One of a series of memoirs Violet Backe wrote about her mother, Nettie.

Anna and Dorothy

Audrey Brown
Inver Grove Heights, Minnesota

"Oh, my, Dorothy, aren't they lovely?" The veined and gnarly hands of Dorothy's mother cupped a bright purple pansy as she leaned closer to view the open-faced flower.

"Yes, Mother, they are nice," Dorothy answered. She surveyed the spreading display of pansies arranged on hip-high tables at Schueller's Greenhouse. She had brought her mother here on a Sunday afternoon outing, to where plastic-covered tents were temporary home to thousands of seedlings set about in tiny boxes of soil.

It was a beautifully warm day, and the musty odor of damp earth permeated the air. Cars and trucks filled the parking area and people wandered up and down the aisles, flat cardboard boxes on one arm, picking, sniffing, choosing. Some shoppers made serious work of buying the traditional tomato and pepper plants, while others clearly plunged ahead, willing to try something new for the coming season. Older children joined their parents, selecting the plants with the biggest blooms. Younger ones tagged behind, a lollipop, thoughtfully provided by the proprietor, bulging in a cheek. They were oblivious to the rows and rows of flowers sparkling with the promise of long summer days ahead.

"I think I'll need about four packs of pansies, Dorothy. I like the purple ones."

"You want them for the garden by the back porch, I suppose." Dorothy said. "You hardly go out there these days."

"Well, you know I always put pansies there," and she shook her head with a definite hint of exasperation.

A light breeze ruffled Anna's puffy white hair, and she released the pansy to pat at her head. A limp, pink sweater pulled across her stooped shoulders, slid to one side as she tipped her head to look up at her daughter. Her smile prompted Dorothy to pick out four packs of the purple pansies, their mock faces bobbing in the gentle wind. Then they moved on to another area.

"My, my, just look at those moss roses, such pretty colors already. Yes . . . I want them for the little garden by the garage. I always put moss roses there; then I could see them every time I take out the garbage."

"But Mother, you never take the garbage out anymore; you know I always do it. I thought we'd fill it with hosta and never have to plant there." Dorothy's eyes rolled upward for a moment, then glanced down at her mother. The lady had folded her hands and was motionless.

Dorothy thought how she had came home to care for her mother after a series of tragic events. She had been widowed four years before, and with her three children all living out-of-state, Dorothy decided to return to her childhood home to care for her long-widowed mother. Her mother's minor car accidents, leaving her almost totally dependent on a wheel chair, were the final factors. Care she must.

Suddenly Dorothy scooped up three packs of moss roses. The fleshy flowers and buds swayed the stout vines.

"Well, Anna, hello. It's nice to see you." The raspy voice belonged to Anna's old neighbor, John.

Anna and Dorothy greeted John with pats and handshakes.

"You still living in your little yellow house?" John leaned his head close to Anna's.

"Oh, yes, you bet, John. I'm still there. Sixty-three years now." Anna's eyes sparkled. "Doing pretty well, thank you."

"Well, Mabel and I are sure glad we moved into our apartment. Miss gardening, though. Just picking up a few geraniums for the windowsill."

"How is Mabel?" Anna looked up, scowling.

"Doing better now; learning how to use her walker. Hip healed real good. Now Dorothy, bring Anna to visit us sometime."

"I will, John—soon, too. Say hello to Mabel for us."

Quick good-byes ended the conversation as busy shoppers squeezed past them to reach for trailing vines and fluffy ferns. Then they, too, moved on.

They passed flats of alyssum, producing the heavy, sweet odor of honey, spread out like a sheet of white before them.

"I remember bordering all my gardens with sweet alyssum, Dorothy. It always looked so fresh, now didn't it?"

"Yes, Mother, you did a fine job with your little gardens," Dorothy said, sighing and brushing a tiny lump of soil from her hand. Her crisp denim skirt was spotless, as was her coordinated plaid shirt. They were her comfort clothes after so many hours dressed in the business suits demanded by her job as a real estate agent. Dorothy only donned jeans when the task required them.

"Now how about some marigolds to put by my vegetable garden. I don't want any bugs, and they keep out bugs, you know." Anna started to pick up a pack of the little yellow flowers, but the pungent odor repulsed Dorothy.

"Mother, really, I don't think you need them. You only have one tomatoe plant and some chives that take care of themselves."

"Oh, all right, Dorothy. You're always telling me what to do lately." She gave an angry push to the box of spicy-scented marigolds, but their sturdy heads only jerked a bit with the shove.

"Ah, the geraniums! Look, look, Dorothy, aren't they fine? Wouldn't your father just love them?" She reached for a plump salmon-colored ball of petals popping out above the mass of green.

"We should have six, at least, Dorothy, and lots of vinca to trail down. Vinca looks so nice in a breeze, like it's alive.

Anna's yellow house had a planter down by the street holding her mailbox. Her husband had built it a few years before he died, and he'd always planted it with geraniums. Anna insisted the practice be continued years after his passing.

"Mother, we only need four; six always made it look too crowded."

"Your father liked six, Dorothy." Anna folded her thin arms across her sunken chest, her elbows making sharp shapes in the pink of the sweater.

Dorothy puckered her mouth into a tight oval of orange lipgloss. Her eyes opened to their roundest, then quickly dropped shut. "Okay, Mother, six it shall be. But no vinca, all right?"

"Fine, fine. I suppose Daddy won't mind."

"Mind?" Dorothy flushed and grabbed up six plants, almost

114

breaking the stems of the heavy flowers. "He'd be relieved to know we have less to care for. Anyway, that does it. We'll have to start planting them this evening."

At the check-out area, Dorothy plopped a second heavy cardboard flat on the counter.

"Wait, wait, Dorothy, aren't you forgetting the morning glories for the back fence, you know, around the garbage can?"

"No, Mother, that trellis fence is too old; it has to be removed. There is a limit to what I can do. At least there should be."

"Yes, honey, there is. You are a fine help to me." Anna slumped a bit in her chair.

"We'll take these, Mrs. Schueller." Dorothy smiled stiffly.

"Hi, Dorothy, how are you? Did you find all the flowers that you wanted?"

"Oh, indeed we did!" Dorothy answered with eyebrows arched.

"And, Anna, how are you? You're looking happy. Are you enjoying your shopping?" Mrs. Schueller bent across the counter in her direction.

"My, yes, you have such a lovely store. I always enjoy coming here every spring. It's one of the things I simply must do." Anna smiled, her yellowed, but perfect dentures overtaking her expression.

After they'd paid for their purchases a young girl carried the flats of plants to Dorothy's car.

They followed her slowly down the cement walk, then began to cross a muddy area where Anna's wheelchair bogged down.

"Hurry, Dorothy, we have a lot to do."

Dorothy bore down on Anna's chair and the wheels made deep, distinct tracks in the softened dirt.

·

Change of Address

Irma M. Schwantes
Fulda, Minnesota

A pproaching the front door of the sprawling brick building, apprehension turning to panic, I wanted to turn and run.

Stepping onto the screened patio, glancing at the orange flowered chairs set in a row against a wall, I tried not to think of the sights, sounds and smells which would greet me just inside the foyer.

This is it. This is THE NURSING HOME! My mother's new home. Other people's mothers go into nursing homes. Friends go into nursing homes. Now my mother had been moved into this nursing home.

It wasn't that I hadn't visited nursing homes many times. My friend Marion had lived in one before she died. I don't remember much about the home she was in, just that I went to visit. The last time was on her forty-eighth birthday. She had a brain deterioration disease. Her mind had regressed to childhood. She got the giggles over every little thing. I sat on the edge of her bed, brushed her hair, and put in some hair bands. I read to her the children's story books I had brought. She laughed through it all. I returned to my car and sat weeping, praying to God to please let her come to heaven soon. She died three days later.

And my friend Connie had been a nursing home resident two and a half years before she died last fall. Connie had no family near, and not a great many friends either. She depended on me. When she could no longer write letters to her sister, I did that for her. I wrote her checks, did her errands. Little things. And she did so much for me. She listened to me. She understood my feelings of helplessness when I told her about my mother's illness. Connie had been my friend for fourteen years. We took shopping trips, and, oh, how Connie loved to shop. She went with me to New Ulm many times to visit my mother. We had enjoyed those excursions and the good apple kuchen Mother would bake for us. Connie had a private room in her nursing home. It was a nice-sized room with a large window to brighten the dreary days. She had her T.V. to watch her favorite soap operas. Her air-concentrater was noisy with it's constant pump-pump, pushing air into her diseased lungs. It kept her alive for two years, two years for us to share. Two years to say all those things friends sometimes are too embarrassed to talk about. We found the meaning of friendship in those months she lay helpless. Her nursing home was bearable, a warm friendly place.

My hand reached for the doorknob. As I neared the information desk, I glanced around the large front room, not really wanting to see. Twenty or thirty wheelchairs were set in rows across the area. I noticed one of the ladies was wearing a sweater just like the one I had given Mother for Christmas. Her hair was uncombed, her mouth was open, drooling. She held one hand up, as a child in school asking to leave the room. She was squinting as she turned her head to follow a passing nurse. BUT THAT IS MY MOTHER!!!

I hesitated before moving in her direction. It felt as if my shoes were stuck in cement. As I bent over her to hug her, she said, "Anita?" 'No Mother. It's me, Irma." I brushed back her once-beautiful, long chestnut brown hair, now turned grey. It hung straight and frizzy. Mother had always worn a hairnet after the waistlength braids had been cut. For all of her ninety-three years she had always cared for her hair and personal hygiene first thing each morning.

I tried not to notice, all the while wanting to shout at someone: is this how it IS here? Oh, how desperately I wanted to scoop her into my arms and run out of this place.

We talked, though she didn't seem to understand much of what I said. When I asked where her room was she pointed at a hall to the right. I wheeled her chair in that direction, a little voice inside telling me to hide my sadness. I pointed out some pretty handcarved wooden wall hangings. I didn't want to look into the tiny rooms. Somewhere along the corridor I became aware of the stench of human excrement. I pretended not to notice. Fleeting glances into rooms revealed residents in various degrees of helplessness. Reaching the end of this hall, we were in a large, bright room with assorted tables and chairs. In one corner a grouping of soft leather chairs was arranged for comfortable visiting. Pushing Mother's chair toward them, I was hoping we could sit and visit, forgetting for a little while that this was not "home." But she said, "This is not my room," paddling her feet furiously, wanting to go someplace.

Turning to go back, we met an aide. I asked her the way to Mother's room. She had to ask me Mother's name! They don't even know Mother's name! Well, Mother had been there less than a week; maybe this girl had not worked a shift yet.

Finally, we reached Mother's room. "Yes this is where I sleep; there is my picture of my family," she said. I squeezed back the tears; the pain in my heart deepened.

Her "place to sleep" was little more than that. A faded green curtain was pulled halfway across the room, separating her half from her roommate's. The curtain screened off most of the light from the large window across the front. A narrow, beige-covered bed was pushed against it, a steel grey floorlamp and small dresser beside it. A plywood closet in the corner held their few possessions. At the end of the closet hung a three-foot mirror at just the right height for Mother to see herself as she paddled by it, not looking. To the left of the door the bathroom protruded leaving just enough space for her roommate to get by with her wheelchair. The only sign of home was the family picture that hung above the dresser. Her alarm clock stood on the dresser. How ironic, I thought. Why would anyone want an alarm clock in this place?

So this is home now! The urge to run intrudes again. I must smile, pretend I am happy for her sake. And so we visit—I, sitting on her bed, she in her wheelchair. She seemed to know now who I am. She asked about Frank, my husband who is recuperating from a badly cut hand. She tells me she is going to have a permanent in the afternoon. She sounds satisfied. Or maybe resigned. Some of the pain is easing in my heart, her words mixing with her thoughts.

Then she told me she had slept in the post office last night. She was there mailing a letter when they locked up, and she was locked in and couldn't get out. My heart grows heavier again. And so the visit went. One moment the talk was of normal everyday things; the next it made no sense at all. Then it was time for her lunch, and I left promising to come back after she had her permanent and afternoon nap.

118

I left without looking back. I lowered my head so passersby would not see my tears.

Later in the afternoon my sister arrived from Iowa, and we went together. Maybe the second time would be less painful. We found her crying, her wheelchair pushed tightly against the bed, caught on the roller. She said "they" kept her in there so long. "They" wouldn't let her out, and she was tired of sitting there. It felt like trying to understand a terror-stricken child. Anita loosened the wheelchair as we hugged her—we looked at each other in confusion.

Her hair was still in rollers, and she was finally able to tell us that she wanted them left in until tomorrow so it would be nice and curly. Anita said, "Let's go and see Aunt Freda." Mother was not excited at the prospect, but if Anita suggested it, she would do it. She had always depended on Anita, as the oldest girl in the family, to make the right decisions. I walked beside them wherever the hall was wide enough. Meeting a nurse or another resident required going single file. It seemed to me this nursing home was smaller than others I had been in, or was it just that I was not as aware then, since it was not MY MOTHER who was there?

Aunt Freda had been in this "home" sixteen years. I had not seen her in the last eight or ten. I was not prepared for how bad she looked. She lay curled into a small ball, looking the size of a ten-year-old child. She said hello, but Mother was again paddling her feet to "go someplace."

Nearby there was a sunny, pretty area with a white wicker settee and two chairs. It looked so inviting, and my body ached, perhaps from driving eighty-five miles that morning, perhaps from the sadness which filled every portion of it. I sat on one of the flowery blue cushioned chairs, hoping Mother would be willing to visit there a while. A pretty yellow canary sang cheerfully in his tiny white cage near the colorful blooming plants. Feeling the special gift of this song brought a smile to my lips. I felt some of the pain leave my heart as I smiled at some of the nearby residents. I saw that some did smile back. Others stared off into space, unaware of the bird's happy song.

As we pushed back toward Mother's room, the long gloomy hallway seemed endless. Mother did not acknowledge that anyone else existed, even though a few residents tried to speak to us. Several times she asked if we would take her home, if only for overnight. We explained again that she had fallen so often that we are not physically able to lift her, that she cannot walk up the four steps to her backdoor.

Soon we were back in her dreary little room. She said she wanted to have a nap then. We called for some aides to help her into bed, and we reluctantly left her. It had not been as painful to leave with my older sister beside me. And yet, getting into her car, I saw through my tears that she too was quietly weeping. "We will miss her," she said. I already do.

CELLAR DOORS AND HOLLYHOCKS: THE SOVEREIGNTY OF MEMORY

Daffodil Pools

Margaret Manship
Mahtomedi, Minnesota

In March one Sunday
I set my feet
In a deep, cold puddle
Sliding and sloshing
Water into my shoes.

The minister stood
By the door of the church
And said
"How do you like
My pool?"

In my ears came back
My mother's voice
After a winter just like this.
On the other side of a puddle
She called us in to supper
"How do you like
My pool?" she said.

"I like it just fine"
I said from long ago
"Almost better than daffodils."

The Census Lady
from *Letters to Katy*

Lucille Arnold
Saint Paul, Minnesota

Dear Katy,

Instead of the census lady coming to your house and turning you, my vivacious, year-and-a-half old granddaughter, into a series of black dots on a piece of paper, the 1980 census came in the mail. No doubt your parents filled out the government forms as to age, sex, color, home ownership and so forth.

As I looked at my census questions, I remembered looking for errors in my 1960 FOSDIC (Filming Optical Sensing Devise for Input to Computers) before the field reviewer came to examine my two weeks' work. Each one of the fourteen hundred ninety-nine persons I had enumerated had been reduced to dots. Now the dots came alive.

Beginning the first of April, 1960, at 9 a.m. I had left the house and started at each northeast corner of the designated blocks I was to cover. There were fewer houses than there are now.

Through a picture window I saw an adorable little girl who seemed to be putting on a booty that was much too small for her. As I rang the doorbell, she straightened up, and I spied a three-month-old baby lying on the floor. The little girl had been trying to put the booty on the baby not on herself. Before I left, they were dots on a piece of paper.

At another house, a four-year-old boy opened the door and shouted, "Mommy the census lady is here." I turned the entire family into dots.

I rewarded an elderly little lady, who apologized for not having some hot coffee ready for me "on such a cold rainy day," by turning her into a cold statistic.

Another elderly lady was concerned because I had slipped on the wet grass and ruined my stockings. She became neat round dots.

At one house the children were being bathed before Daddy came home. One cute little girl came and sat beside me in her birthday suit. I stripped her further before her mother called sharply, "Come here."

At another house a distinguished man proudly showed me his birth certificate hanging on the wall. He said, "I was born in Germany in 1889. Once I owned this whole block." I turned him into a statistic so he looked exactly like the little nude girl.

One woman greeted me with, "You're coming into my house and it's such a mess. My son has been painting and decorating. He made every bit of this furniture." Books and dishes were placed neatly on the dining room table. Some of the furniture had been temporarily moved into a bedroom. I was glad the woman hadn't seen the mess I had left in my house that morning.

After I had turned another woman and her son into dots, she grabbed my hand and said, "Come and see how nice my bedroom looks. My son just painted it. Can't you stay for a cup of coffee?" I didn't have time for a cup of coffee. I was being paid for reducing people to dots.

My heart ached as I walked into the Skalbeck house. Our friend Archie had just died. How could I make him a statistic?

Grabbing her small son after I had rung the doorbell, one woman said, "Johnny, you CANNOT go out." Turning to me she said, "I hope you've had the mumps." Forlornly, Johnny watched the neighborhood children through the picture window. Was the bright sun intensifying his red hair, freckles and his swollen creeks? I asked, "Are you grumpy because you're mumpy?" He snickered before he became dots.

Then there was the henna-haired, middle-aged woman who was unaware that youth is like quicksilver: the tighter it is held, the easier it escapes. On my third call back she still refused to give me her age—only finally to give it graciously to the supervisor over the telephone.

There had been times I had to go out after supper, like the last evening of the second week. I was so tired I wondered if I could make it to the next house. A woman in a wheelchair opened the door. She said, "I wish I could walk like that." Quickly I sent up a thank you to God and forgot about my aching feet.

How I would love to have a leisurely cup of coffee with the lonely women of 1960, if they are still alive. I wonder if the cute little nude girl has turned into an attractive young woman wearing Jordache jeans. It would be fun to find out if the grumpy, mumpy little boy turned into a man with grumpy, mumpy kids of his own.

When I finally answered the 1980 questions that came in the mail, I wondered if any of the people I had enumerated in 1960 remembered the census lady who had come to their doors and turned them into dots.

I suppose the 1990 census will be done by pushing buttons. If I'm still on this earth, you and I may look alike. Perhaps we'll have numbers that designate we are related to each other. The lonely women won't have a chance to offer the census lady a cup of coffee. The cute little kids won't know that once upon a time there were census ladies who turned them into dots.

Love,

Nana

Cellar Doors and Hollyhocks

Helen Foster
Rochester, Minnesota

I t is a warm morning. A quiet morning. The air is still. Even from off the nearby lake, there is no breeze. The sky is overcast, and I have a feeling that it will hang like that all day.

The birds sing independently, each in his own key, and I wonder at their melodic song when there is no apparent effort toward harmony. I hear footsteps crunching along the sandy lane. A screen door squeaks open and closes again with a hushed click. In the distance there is a dull rumble that could be thunder or a car crossing the rickety bridge over the inlet. From the seclusion of my sundeck I listen to these sounds of summer, soft, yet distinct, for the acoustics are very good this morning.

My delphiniums stand tall and quite elegant on this breezeless morning. The cranberry bush is growing tiny cranberries, and the flowering begonias are actually flowering. Not bad, I tell myself, for someone who puts a seed into the ground and cares not whether she sees it again.

I remember the day last spring when I planted them. Blissfully, I had picked and chosen and loaded the trunk of my car at the garden shop. When the salesgirl totaled my purchases, I was aghast at the amount I had spent. What's done is done . . . but what if they don't live? Before the answer came to me, I asked myself another question: whatever happened to the old give-and-take flower gardens that we once knew?

Someone would thin a bed of lillies of the valley and trade the extra ones for a few roots of phlox. When the sweet William spread into the tomato plants, it was dug up and exchanged for a peony clump or a bleeding heart starter slip.

So, whatever the variety, everyone in the block had the same assortment. Everyone had sunflowers growing around their trash burners, and hollyhocks alongside their cellar doors. Only the size and shape of the gardens varied. Some were in the form of a star, some crescent-shaped and some, like my mother's, were simply a border around the vegetable garden.

Looking back, I can't recall my mother ever actually handing

126

out money for plants or shrubs—except maybe a package of nasturtium seeds, or perhaps a geranium or two for Decoration Day. But mostly it was lilacs that we carried to the cemetery. Armfuls of them. Heaven knows we had plenty of lilacs, and it was "old Herm" we had to thank for them.

Old Herm was a neighbor who lived across the alley and down a couple houses. Herm led a now-you-see-him-now-you-don't sort of existence. Or, as my father used to put it, "About every so often, old Herm had to go on a bender." So Herm's disappearing acts were something we took for granted, but his reentry into the real world was met with far more concern. It was as if my parents knew no preventive measures, but once he was home again they surely knew how to make him feel welcome.

Early in the morning on the first day of his return, Herm would be in his backyard, wearing a clean blue shirt and fresh overalls, and whacking away at his lilac bushes. As though he'd been waiting for this cue, my father would fill a thermos with coffee, grab two cups from the cupboard, and head for Herm's place where the two of them would sit on tree stumps, drink the strong, hot coffee and visit for maybe a half hour or more. When, after a time, my father had to leave for work, Herb would pick up his ax and go back to the lilac bushes.

Shortly before noon, my mother would fill a fruit jar with her end-of-the-garden soup and across the alley we'd go. Each time Herm would ask one of us children to set it inside the kitchen, and my mother would point to the fallen lilac bushes and say, "If you want, we'll be happy to take those off your hands." Herm would say he had no other plans for them and my mother would say, "Thank you," and Herm would say, "Thank you," and we'd spend the rest of the day planting lilac bushes.

One time Herm told my father, "Your Missus is a nice lady. She don't run around wearing a lot of "rooj" like some women do."

This was high praise coming from someone who stayed clear of people in general and women, in particular.

Herm had had a wife at one time. It had been rumored that she was high-spirited and had "run away." I think it would not be unfair to assume that she wore "rooj." More than that, you wouldn't have to be a sleuth to figure out that she was the one who had planted all those lilac bushes in the first place.

"Maybe that's why the poor old guy drinks," my father said more than once. Sometimes my mother suggested it might be the other way around, that she ran away because he drank. "But either way," she would add, "it's not a reason – only an excuse."

Although my mother was not all heart in this matter, she continued carrying the fruit jars of soup to Herm, and she never stopped planting the discarded lilac roots. And so the hedge got thicker and longer, and pretty soon it ran the length of our lot and half way down the other side.

Now I never knew if Herm watched that hedge of lilacs grow to such proportion and then came to see it as an ominous reminder, or whether he just plain got sick of my mother's end-of-the-garden soup. Either way, the "benders" seemed to occur less and less frequently until they just didn't happen at all anymore. Finally, Herm hung up his ax, and when he did, it seemed he hung up all his frustrations and resentments, too.

The persistent revving of a chain saw motor jolts me back to the present. I move into the kitchen which is, after all, the original and most logical room in a house for remembering. Why this is I'm not sure, but I have an idea that it has something to do with the things we keep and cling to in the kitchen.

A friend of mine redecorates, restores and refurnishes her home with the change of each season, but in her kitchen she uses a flour sifter which has long since lost its rotary handle. She thumps it with the heel of her hand, forcing the flour through the bent and tattered screen. Her grandmother used that sifter to make soda bread, and it holds a lot of memories for her. And so it is with my mother's blue bowl.

Today it sits on my cupboard top – a home for a banana and a couple of oranges. Discolored and pitted, its usefulness is limited. But, I don't really see it this way.

What I see is a bright blue, basket-weave bowl filled with beef and noodles and placed in the center of a porcelain top table. I see my father at the kitchen sink scrubbing his face and neck with sudsy hands. Never with a wash cloth. That would have been "sissy." Crying, too, was considered sissy in those days, but when my grandfather died, my father just went ahead and

128

cried anyway. I felt sad then, but guilty too, because my mind was on another problem.

For weeks I had been studying my lines for a home talent play and now there was a good chance I wouldn't be allowed to take part. The first presentation was to take place the day after my grandfather's funeral, and how would it look for me to appear on stage during this time of mourning. When it was decided that Grandpa wouldn't have wanted me to give it up, I was elated but scared because I had missed five rehearsals.

As it turned out, I came off far better than the leading lady, whose name was Bubbles. Bubbles was a flashy blonde who traveled with "the company" and was the leading lady wherever the show landed. She was also old—at least 25.

During one of her dances, Bubbles was supposed to swoop low under a bird cage, and although she'd probably done this a hundred times or more, this night she didn't swoop low enough. To this day, I can see that wig dangling from the bird cage while Bubbles circles the stage, dauntlessly. The audience roared while the cast giggled in the wings.

Again, back to the blue bowl and the fruit which should not have been allowed to wither. From the garden shop to old Herm and his problems, from beef and noodles to a wig and a bird cage. Nothing gained. Nothing accomplished. Some may even call it wasted time.

"But why not?" I asked myself.

"Sure," I answered. "Why not!"

And so, from this simple philosophy a host of memories have surfaced. Some are happy, some not so happy, others only immaterial, but all of them worth renewing.

excerpt from
Farmer in the Dells

Richard Lee Fields
Mankato, Minnesota

I t didn't make headlines in my old hometown, but in the late
summer of '68 I took my wife and kids on one last vacation
trip. At the time I didn't know it was the last trip, but it kind of
felt that way. It turned out to be a hopeless attempt to shape up
a faltering marriage, perhaps shape up tentative parenthood—a
last roll of the marital dice, but at least I made the attempt. It
came up snake eyes.

A half dozen years later, on a business trip around the first of
April, I found myself calling on a customer north of the Dells,
with the famed Wisconsin Dells cruise boats and Tommy Bart-
lett's water-show extravanganzas open to family trade. I found
myself gawking with deja vu eyes at the countryside, confusing
business with bemused hindsight, as I came down Highway 13
to visit briefly—just in and out—this one particular stopover
made by my still-intact family on that final vacation trip. The
business call was finished. I could unreel a casual spin through
the Dells. Be objective, I told myself, no profound thinking; stay
in the present while coolly appraising the past, indulging neither change of expression nor change of heart. Pump no exces-
sive oxygen into lifeless memories. Wave in passing. I needed
to get gas anyway, and it was time for lunch, so why not? Go
ahead and bury the dead. Doesn't hurt to pick at a sore once in
a while if it's already pretty well scarred over—if you don't dig
too deep. It shouldn't take long before getting back out on Inter-
state 90 for the roll down to Madison. A travelling man stops every day for gas and lunch, one place or another. The stops kind
of run together, like barbeque and bicarbonate. So what the
hell?

Besides, I thought, what can I expect to see that could re-open
any tombs? All these places—vacationland, joyland, toyland—
they all seem pretty much the same. Las Vegas has no monop-
oly on garishness. Take in Carefreeland in '68, then see it again
a half-dozen years later. It simply seems snagged in your mind

130

like a time warp, caught up on barbs of old hat film. Frayed and flickering but still true to the first time around. A morass of memory that wants to drag you back down, if you get careless while slogging around in the quicksands of old haunts. But not for me. Others might let themselves be affected that way. Sip the indulgent mead of melancholia, hail the bittersweet. To each his own, but all I wanted was just a look. No postmortem.

I pulled in at the Family Coffee Shoppe. The concrete aprons were freshly swept, plenty of bright orange neon tubing abloom around the windows and along the eaves, an air of just-back-from-the-cleaners about it. When I entered, I found all the furniture covered with sheet plastic. The renovating crew working were leisurely sweeping up. They froze in place astride their brooms at my intrusion.

"Ain't open yet, mister."

"Sign's on."

"Just checkin' her out. Guess I'd better turn her out."

I retreated, figuring I had merely hit a late-opening cafe accidentally—already it was the first of April with primaries coming on and pickups were thick on the highway—but I was wrong. Other places around there were still closed, too.

I got back in the car and tooled slowly along, giving it the old windshield appraisal. Obviously the area was still feeling the effects of one of those yawning, doorstep-lingering winters. Most of the gas-fed flowers weren't in bloom yet, no blinking red or orange daffadowndillies set afire and wreathing around the eaves, no animated waves of white light zooming endlessly from left to right on the billboards, beckoning the delights of Alpine villages just beyond. Candyland's oozing chocolate lava was still gelled in place. The tracks of a lone snowmobile snailed over the roadside ditch.

A ten-foot statue of an Indian chief stood alongside the road. His massive war bonnet trailed behind his head; it plummeted down his back to the knees, the splintered quills were ashen. He stood there majestically, locked stiff in petrified wood, glaring down on instrusive passersby, arms folded, jutting jaw, scowling. I slowed the car.

"See," I said, "I had a family here, once."

He seemed to stare right through me, suspended in time, passive, stoic—they're supposed to be like that, aren't they—unmoved. His stare seemed to say, "I had a whole tribe here, once. At least you are white. Grow yourself another family. That's easy. Try finding a lost tribe."

The Indian chief and I gazed at each other. A thought materialized between us. "No camp is permanent." Well, the chief ought to know.

I wondered what he thought about all the noble genuine Indian trading shoppes. They, too, remained closed as yet; so were the pinball galleries and the souvenir stands—shuttered, battened down. Last year's brittle leaves were still trapped in tattered flounce against the curbs. An air of winterized immobility lingered along the main street, an arthritis of absentee ownership. A palpable somnambulism hovered over the empty benches and the vacated motels. The few people out on the streets seemed in no hurry to go any place; they had to be natives. Deserted playgrounds seem more barren than unplowed prairies.

Ticket windows at the boat docks were chained and locked with padlocks. Four large cruise boats were beached in a row on the bank above the water—castrated whales, stranded abeam. A fellow wearing a jacket leaned against the prow of one, smoking a pipe, studying the gravel at his feet.

Well, I was getting a look, but I didn't care much for gray silhouette. If I wanted more mellow-yellow, I'd have to do a little mental dredging, try to recall more of the braze of that golden August in '68.

I remembered a restaurant that my daughter Susan, then 16, had enjoyed, Call of the Wild, across the highway from the Paul Bunyan place. I could call the home office from there. Let them know I was working, making calls, writing orders. Keep those commission checks flowing in. Keep those alimony checks flowing out.

I drove there for lunch, thinking I'd rekindle a little masochistic nostalgia, a minor flagellation to whip up the old juices. She liked it once, okay, I'd try to like it again, all over again just for old times' sake—for when my daughter was still the family daughter. I'd see whether I could pick out the very table where we sat, see it somehow through Susan's eyes. Maybe I'd talk to her Banquo's chair while I ate, wondering why she had liked this place enough to comment on it, before she was a high school senior, before Purdue, before marriage. Before she stopped making comments.

Back then we still made comments—fair or foul—but at least we made comments to each other. All of us, for that matter. Like President Kennedy said, "There's time for making comments, and there's time to stop making comments."

Like: "Why Purdue, for God's sake?" I made that one. To my wife. "That's across the state line! Why not Illinois, or Bradley, or Illinois State? Do you realize what the tuition will be?"

"Because," my wife said, "boys outnumber girls ten to one there."

She was right, of course. I don't mean about the enrollment percentages; I don't know about that. But Susan found her husband there. A chemical engineer and computer science major who talks over my head. When we talk.

But the Call of the Wild was still closed for the season, and so was Paul Bunyan.

So I backtracked and picked up Highway 23; we had come in from the south that way, back in '68. I drove down through the southern part of Wisconsin Dells, driving past the massive undulating slides that scared me then, and still do, past Secnes from Bibleland and peeling billboards advertising Yogi Bear and Jellystone Park.

Suddenly I spotted the stock car racetrack. That had to be the racetrack on which my son Rickie, an adventurous 12, mistakenly managed to drive out in front of the high school boys on the first turn of his first ride ever on such a track—and then he couldn't figure out what to do about it.

I could see him, wide-eyed, staring straight ahead with his foot paralyzed on the accelerator, leading the pack around the first lap, plainly frightened. It had confirmed immediately my wife's vehement "No" vote when he had clamored to try out racing in the small Indy-type cars, claiming knowledge of them and promising caution way beyond his twelve years. I guess all twelve-year-olds are supremely confident, aren't they? It takes teens to bring the onset of anxiety, along with acne. But Richie was a cocky twelve, raised on a TV diet of Supermouse. He dashed through the turnstile in a flash when Dad weakened and said, "Okay, go ahead." And there he was, obviously alarmed in front of all the hotrodders behind him. But he was determined to hang on, straddling the middle of the track so that the jammed-up pack behind him couldn't get around. Not, that is, until he finally came to his senses and eased over to the outside, letting everyone go zinging past him on the inside. He came back to us after his harried drive with as much insouciance as he could muster—a pintsized dissembler wearing braces and a happy grin. I was grinning, too. My son the hot dog!

My wife glared at me. "Hope you're satisfied!"

"More importantly, I hope Richie's satisfied. He did fine."

"Never scared me at all, Dad," Richie crowed. But he took my hand, and held it a while. He hadn't done that since he was five.

I wondered, if Richie were with me in the car now, if he would remember. Sure he would. And still claim an adolescent bravado. He even claimed bravado about the divorce. "Things'll work out, Dad."

Gooseberries

Mary Schwarz
Saint Paul, Minnesota

When I was young
there were gooseberries
growing in our backyard.
We called them
Stachelbeeren (thornberries).
They made my tongue bristle
but I liked them
the way I like people
who are outspoken.

In my needlepoint days
I favored the strawberry.
With its emerald crown it
triumphed over the faded
gooseberry on a spiny stem.

Gooseberries in a backyard
are as rare as
old-fashioned modesty.
Served in an antique bowl
they even look pretty.

No Longer a Place

Margaret Brawley
Gatzke, Minnesota

T he cotton field stretched as far as the eye could see. She
could only imagine how it would be to get to the other side.
As near-sighted as she was, it was hard to make out the other
workers—some white, some black, working desperately to
finish the field before darkness came and stopped them.

There had been a school on this farm for the black kids to at-
tend after the crops had all been gathered. Later the white
sharecropper, with his wife and six kids, needed a home. So the
farm owner closed the school, and let them live there. There
were only two rooms. The big front classroom served as living,
dining and bedroom for the whole brood, and the smaller lean-
to-room, formerly the cloakroom, became the kitchen.

Margaret lived there. She was the oldest of the six—not a very
pretty child and skinny to the point of emaciation. Her only
playground had been the cotton fields, where she worked with
her mother irrigating and chopping weeds from the tiny cotton
plants.

The water used for irrigation was hard and brakish and the
salt residue glistened in the sun. Year after year the salt grew
more and more dominent until finally the cotton wouldn't grow
there anymore. The field was abandoned to the salt cedar and
mesquite trees. Even grass would not root there for years after.
The same canels that brought water to the fields also brought
drinking water to the family and to the few cows kept to provide
their milk and butter.

The cows belonged to the landowner. All the family received
for tending them was the milk and butter. And when they were
dry, there was no milk for the six kids.

Margarets' mother, Carrie, was twenty-eight years old. With
six kids and another on the way, she felt overwhelmed by all the
responsibilities she had had to assume at such an early age. She
was seventeen when Howard came into her life. He looked so
dashing and handsome. He was thirty-four, and owned a car.
She had never ridden in a car before. At that time he worked on

a railroad that was coming to their area. In 1920 that was still a big event. It held great promise to the local farmers — it was a way to get crops to market.

Papa had warned her, even threatened a beating if she so much as spoke to a railroader. The glamour of them was too much. One night with "shoes in hand," she ran away with the handsome man. And though for sixty years she would love him with a passion, and bear him twelve children, her life would always be hardscrabble poor. Sometimes when she had the migraine headaches and there was not even aspirin to dull the pain, she would long to be a child again in her papa's house.

Margaret was the near-sighted one. As eldest, even before she was old enough for school she had been a "rocker of babies' — washing the tiny faces, diapering them with whatever scrap of cloth was handy. There were no gleaming white diapers, just scraps of cloth from old dresses or skirts that could no longer be worn. Standing on a stool, Margaret washed the breakfast dishes, while Mama cooked supper, and the supper dishes while Mama cooked breakfast. There was never enough kerosene to use the lamp at night for dishwashing.

The old school house never had screens on the windows. At night Howard would bring in a few scraps of cotton lint that always hung on the tumbleweeds lining the fence rows. He put it into a small smudge pot and let it smoulder to make a thick smoke so mosquitoes would stay out of the room. Thereafter, whenever Margaret smelled a piece of cloth burning, she was transported back in time to that one room, crowded with the sound and smell of unwashed bodies, fussy childen and weeping women.

Howard was always optimistic about next year. Always he was going to make a "bale of cotton to the acre" next year. Never mind if this year was almost total failure. From springtime until late fall, there was nothing but hard, back-breaking labor with no money coming in. Always there was the bank, looking over his shoulder, demanding their pound of flesh.

No wonder then that he turned to alcohol, never realizing what a hole he was digging for the entire family. When he went to town to ask for groceries on credit, or asked for more money at the bank, he fortified his courage with drink—trying to deaden his self-loathing with liquor.

He was a kind man, he never physically abused his family except by the gnawing hunger and tired bodies they all had to endure. But he was selfish in a way he could not imagine, for each drink he took removed food from his family, and it took away his respect. It was many years before Margaret could see that her father was only human—that his drinking only partially covered up the shame, frustration and overwhelming sadness he felt for exposing his wife and children to the drudgery and bone chilling want they all faced. It was a world he did not create, could not change and would not tolerate sober.

For Carrie it was an even worse time. No mother can stand to see her children deprived of the very essence of life. To see them hungry, cold and near-naked was more than she could bear. So, leaving the babies with Margaret, she went into the cotton fields herself.

Using the old horses and cultivators, broken and hay-wired together, Carrie tilled the fields, hoeing and pulling the dirt up onto the lister ridges, saving what precious moisture there was. The wind blew day after day, whipping the sandy soil into raging dust storms, turning the wheel of the windmill into a ring of fire. The barbed wire fences were alive with electricity absorbed from the dry air. There was no hope of rain and there was not one thing in the world she could do to make it better.

Margaret spent her days tending babies, washing dishes, carrying clean water in and dirty water out, never knowing there was a different world. All the girls she knew wore the same plaid dresses from the WPA office, carried the same patted meat, or peanut butter, on biscuits to school for lunch. That is, after they were allowed to start school, usually following Thanksgiving.

Margaret was not a good student. She sat silently in the back of the room, hoping the teacher would not call on her, never realizing that there was a reason she didn't see and that it had a name—myopia. She didn't know other kids saw things clearer than she.

One day, on impulse she wrote a note to the teacher saying that even to herself the jumble of letters she copied from the blackboard didn't make sense, not like when she copied from a book. But it was what she saw up there. Mrs. Reed cried over the note—cried for the child who could not see, cried for herself because she had not taken the time to know the child and her problems. She thought Margaret was stupid because of the way she lived. She cried because of the time in history in which these children lived. Then she went to the local Lions Club and pleaded for glasses for the girl. She was as happy as if it were her own child when Margaret told her it was the first time she had known that trees had leaves like cotton did.

From that time on books were to become Margaret's lifeline, the written word was forever wonderful. That all humankind's history, ambitions, hopes and dreams were written down to be studied, marveled at, and understood was more than she could comprehend.

When Margaret, a grown woman, read "Directive" by Robert Frost—"There is a house that is no more a house/Upon a farm that is no more a farm/And in a town that is no more a town"— she realized that other generations had lived poor. And now, when she is old, she knows that life has come full circle.

Winter is here again on the northern plains where Margaret lives. Snow lies like a blanket protecting the soil below—resting, renewing, saving energy until spring comes again. She stands barefoot, in her old familiar flannel robe, drinking the day's first cup of coffee. Watching the sun creep over the horizon, spreading a pink and yellow stain over the snowy landscape. She marvels again at how truly wonderful God's world really is.

She wonders what the farmers will do now, caught as Howard was years ago by a credit crunch. She knows that some will lose all. Some will persevere and win. And she prays, "Please God let there be no place where laughter and play are small islands in a sea of work, and where poets 'Weep for what little things could make them glad!' "

DRY BONES: CYCLES OF LOSS AND HEALING

Fallen Leaves, Hidden Heart

Roy Benjamin Moore
Mankato, Minnesota

We drive through the cemetery gate
then wait beside the narrow way
that winds within this quiet place.
You hold my hand,
understanding my two lives, two wives—one gone.
You bid me go.
The autumn sky is grey—
no breeze to sway the bare-branched trees,
nor stir the layered leaves
that grace the ground of graveyard scene.
I hear no sound until I trudge—
Swish—
    Swish—
        Swish—
wading through those shoe-high leaves,
leaves fallen from the maple trees
that once spread shade on graves below.
Now, no flat low marking stone in sight
beneath this autumn's yellow coverlet.
Again I walk—
Swish—
    Swish—
        Swish—
And come, it seems, to hers
with her bare tree above.
I scrape away the golden screen—
I see her name—again I feel her love
and then I wish—
Such futile yearning. So I turn—
      —Swish
    —Swish
—Swish
back to where I am
and where we are.

The Magic Potion

Leah S. Haas
Deerwood, Minnesota

T he large leaded glass bottle that stood on the dresser in my Grandma Trites' downstairs bedroom had a glass stopper and a purple ribbon tied around the bottle neck. In it was the "very best of camphor," for that was Grandma's favorite remedy. The bottle had survived only by chance and had a place of honor on the old-fashioned dresser which my dad, Lewis Trites, had purchased for his mother with this first paycheck when he was seventeen.

That was the year their farmhouse had burned in the March wind. The roof had kindled from sparks blown over from the smoke shack where sides of pork were being made ready for summer eating. Pa Trites had gone to town, and the younger children were in school. It had been an unusually dry spring in Illinois. Lewis was out in the field when he saw the smoke. Pulling the horses to a stop, he ran for the house. Taking the stairs two at a time, his one thought was of the boxes of arrowheads and Indian artifacts that he and his two brothers, John and Van, had picked and dug from the farmland. The collection, in large wooden boxes, was stacked nearly to the ceiling in the upstairs hall. Grabbing one, he ran back down the stairs, but the flames were already starting to eat through the roof and the smoke was heavy. It was impossible to go back for more. His mother was standing on a chair in the kitchen taking her good dishes from the top shelves of the cupboard. She called to Lewis to carry them out as she took them down. Along with the dishes, the camphor bottle was saved from the flames.

I remember how the camphor seemed like a magic potion. Whether it was a mosquito bite or a scratch from a raspberry bush, Grandma would say, "Child, go put a bit of camphor on it." I would go into the bedroom and, standing on my tiptoes, carefully take the stopper from the bottle and daub a little on the offending place. The bedroom was unused and the bed very neat with its white counterpane. There were lace curtains on the window and the room was cool and quiet. To me, as a little girl, it was like entering a shrine for healing. My little injuries were always made better immediately.

After I grew up, I looked many times for a leaded glass bottle like the old bottle Grandma had on the dresser, but I've never found one. However, with the years I've realized it was not the bottle, nor even the camphor, but rather the love and concern Grandma had over our least hurt that was really the important ingredient of the magic potion.

Several years ago, I was sorting out some family photographs and I came across one of my brother Bruce, my sister Eloise and me when we were small. On the back of it in Grandma's shaky hand was written, "My dear, dear grandchildren." As I looked at the inscription, I could once again hear her say, "Child, go put a bit of camphor on it."

Christmas Eve

Mary M. McBride
Edina, Minnesota

I t was Christmas Eve, and Dad still wasn't home. I was a little worried because the bakery would be closed in a while, and he'd promised he would take me to get a gingerbread man. Every Christmas season Dad took us kids to this particular bakery which a client of his owned, and which had absolutely the best gingerbread in all of Omaha. I can still smell the wonderful aroma of cinnamon and ginger, feel the warmth of the ovens, and see the rows and rows of cookies. The gingerbread men were huge, sprinkled with colored sugar, their candy eyes wide open as if to see the world. They were dressed like soldiers with shiny raisin buttons and were all lined up in formation like an army. It was an agony to choose. Did the one third from the left have more buttons, or was the top one bigger? My brother and sister always went along, too, and I had to choose carefully so as to get one bigger than theirs. At last the selection would be made, and the baker would put them in a white paper bag, tucking in an extra round cookie for us to eat on the way home. Dad then made us put them on the fireplace mantel above our stockings until Christmas day when we finally could eat them. I usually nibbled mine and tried to make it last until the end of the day, but I rarely made it.

For me, the anticipation was more gratifying than the event. I tingled waiting for Christmas morning when we could open our presents, unload our stockings, and eat the gingerbread soldiers. I didn't want any deviation from the ritual and felt sorry for my friends who peeked at their presents beforehand; they spoiled all the delicious excitement of anticipation.

Tonight I was getting apprehensive, wondering where he was. I could feel the unspoken tension in the house, although no one was saying anything about it. My mother was wrapping a few last-minute presents, my sister playing quietly with her stuffed animals, and my brother reading as usual. No one else seemed anxious. Maybe I was worrying unnecessarily. I knew he closed his law office at noon, and he'd probably stopped at the club. He wouldn't forget the trip to get the gingerbread men—it was a Christmas tradition.

Nonetheless, I couldn't help remembering other Christmases when he was late coming home Christmas Eve. On those nights when he did come home, he went right to bed. This time it would be different, I told myself; he had promised. When he finally arrived, long after the bakery had closed, my heart sank. He talked funny, slurred and had a strange smile on his face, like he knew a secret. He didn't go right to bed, but stayed up awhile talking to us. My mother was tight-lipped, and I dreaded the fighting that I knew was coming. I always hid my head under the covers and put my hands over my ears—but I heard them anyway. I couldn't hear the words, but I heard the screaming, and the angry tone of voice. Maybe they'd get a divorce, and then what would happen to me? The terror of that thought cut through me like a icy knife, and I quickly turned it aside.

I wished he'd go to bed. I didn't know what was wrong, but I knew something was. I was embarrassed because he was different, silly, and I was a little afraid of him. This wasn't the kind father I usually saw. Then he took me aside and said he wanted me to go to the garage with him. I didn't know what he might do to me and I was scared, but no one else seemed to notice. Maybe I was crazy, just imagining the whole scene. He insisted, so reluctantly I accompanied him to the garage. There in front of me was a brand new bicycle, my first full-sized one, my Christmas present. He still had that funny expression on his face, pleased. I pretended I was thrilled, but all I was thinking was how to get him back in the house.

Finally, I cajoled him back in and made an excuse to go to my room. Christmas was ruined for me. I hated knowing what I was getting; it spoiled all the anticipation and excitement and made it just like getting school clothes. I hated the tension in the house, which I blamed my mother for. If she didn't make such a big deal of his stopping off at the club, if she wouldn't fight with him, it would be all right. And I worried about me. If they did get a divorce, I would have to go live with my father. He would need me to take care of him. My mother could take care of herself, and even though I would rather live with her, someone would have to look after Dad. I was eight years old, the oldest girl, and clearly the one to do it.

The fight that night was the worst one yet. I crawled deep under the covers and plugged my ears, but it wasn't good enough. I went to sleep with the sounds of screaming, crying and fighting. The next day, Christmas, we opened our gifts in the morning and drove to Lincoln to have Christmas dinner with our grandparents, Dad's parents. Dad had forgotten he'd shown me the bike, so I pretended to be surprised, and I really was thrilled to get it. No one mentioned the previous evening, and I began to think I dreamed it, or that maybe I was crazy because no one else had noticed. I doubted my perceptions since I seemed to be the only one to see what was going on. We never did talk about it.

Next Year in Jerusalem

Mara Joseph
Roseville, Minnesota

W e were both inmates of the Women's House of Detention in New York's Greenwich Villege in the early '50s.

From barred windows, we could look down at the street vegetable vendors, tops of cabbages and yellow taxicabs our only bit of color; pimps shouting up to the "girls," ambulance and police sirens our only sounds of the city.

My duties were in the chapel, dusting, putting up the prayer books. Later, I was promoted to the private quarters of the prison administrator, still dusting, graduated to mopping.

Somewhere . . . somewhere . . . it must be raining violets. Here it was raining.

I looked forward to each day when an hour's recreation on the roof was possible. While others played punch ball or joined their lesbian friends for a smoke, I found my way to the one quiet bench — Willa Cather's "Death Comes for the Archbishop" for sustenance.

She was there, petite, gentle, sometimes knitting with those clumsy, prison-issue, soft-spine plastic needles — more often just staring, her large black eyes trying to focus on an unknown future.

My conversation caused some apprehension, at first.

She was natually suspicious of anyone who came too close, seeking her company more than the others. But soon she shared something of herself: thoughts of children, sometimes speaking of her parents, her brother, her husband, reading a paragraph or two from his letters, written in love from The Tombs, the men's prison where, dependent on her courage and strength, he wrote almost poetically. Shared tensions were relieved by news of his most recent conversations with lawyers, guardedly told; looking forward to their next opportunity of being together, albeit publicly, when they next met with attorneys.

An unwritten rule of prison life protected our beginning friendship: never inquire into a pending trial unless your counsel was solicited.

She needed nothing of this from me. The two-day-old newspapers I was able to read in the library were vivid enough. She was the prison's most notorious inmate. I knew she knew I knew.

We became sisters, looking for each other every day, needing each other every day. If it restored dignity, made us comb our hair, kept language alive, it was nourishment beyond prison fare. We spoke of aspirations and longings, prayer written into words like "hope" and "wish" and "someday."

Woman talk. So many ethnic and cultural interests to discover and share. Household hints and anecdotes of children and school and old neighborhoods. Overheard, we would have sounded like a story conference for a women's magazine.

It was now Easter. Good women of the community heralded the holidays at the chapel service, the Christian aura of guilt and resurrection swollen with special meaning in these disciplinary confines.

We were both Jewish. As we approached our own Passover holiday, we missed the security of family tables and history recited one more time. Together, we dared to talk to the administrator and found her very receptive to a Seder for the 16 Jewish women within the walls.

Longchamps Restaurant had graciously agreed to cater. Planning the menu and the service was left to us. Prostitutes, forgers, shoplifters, child abusers; a car thief; a customs-violator; and Ettie, waiting in custody for federal trial, set our table as though we were our own grandmothers—with a resourceful ritual proscription, remembering everything. The first white linen tablecloth I had seen in months; there the roasted eggs, there the parsley for Spring, matzohs to be hidden later, the familiar grape "wine." A woman who had been imprisoned for three years trembling as she placed the shank bone of lamb, the horseradish and "charosset" on the ceremonial place. The polished wine goblet for Elijah, candles ready for the lighting and the blessing; flowers, nuts, raisins, the bitter and the sweet. Were there really matzoh balls and chicken soup, honey and sponge cake?

Our prison uniforms, twice laundered, seemed immaculate.

150

Some of us wore handkerchiefs, with a bit of tatting, on our heads, or a bit of lace covering borrowed from the chapel.

Ettie's was the "father's" chair, provided with pillows – our custom of reclining at ease, like a Roman freeman during his meal.

She led the Seder, the traditional order of the meal, from Haggadahs supplied to us by a city synagogue, reciting the plagues that had befallen our enemies, repeating the annually told tale of the flight from Egypt, and singing the songs of Passover.

The voice! A sweet, almost professional soprano, a pure woman's strain of age-old sadness mixed with joy – the gloriously inherited "nuzach" of centuries.

The celebration was over. We blew out our candles, stacked our dishes as we did it in the mess hall, thanked the matron who had been the gentile at our table, as is the custom. We wished one another "good luck" in our individual appeals and returned to our floors, still alone, a little less lonely.

We had marked the day as Jews have been doing, in enslavement and freedom, everywhere, for thousands of years. The youngest of us had asked the "four questions." Judges, juries, district attorneys had nothing to do with the answers.

I remember Ettie each year at Passover. Remembering adds special meaning to my repetition of the "age-old" story. She would have been a senior citizen now. A grandmother.

Ethel Rosenberg. She was taken to Sing Sing prison in Ossinging, in upstate New York, there to be executed.

I read over and over again how she resisted death by burning minutes longer than her husband, how she leaned over and thanked and kissed the matron who had befriended her on Death Row, how she died convicted of espionage against our country – betrayed by the brother of whom we had once talked.

Goodbye, Ettie. It was just Passover again. I have put away the special dishes. One broke as we danced around the table.

I hear you singing. You added your own special resonance to the cry, "Next year in Jerusalem . . . "

This piece first appeared in the St. Paul Dispatch Pioneer Press on April 12, 1987.

Sonnet for March

Meg Kramer
Truman, Minnesota

I said, look long and carefully today;
Note well the form of leafless bush and tree
For now the days are few in which to see
Stark beauty in each branch along the way.
Even now new buds are swelling day by day;
And soon elm flowers will beckon to the bee.
Green rafter branches, spread in grove and lea
Meet overhead, cathedral like, in May.
But now exposed to view, the form laid bare,
Exquisite lines of twig and branch and limb
Delight the eye in March's chilly air,
From gnarled oak to maple tapering slim.
Some grant no beauty in a naken tree,
It seems near perfect loveliness to me.

Rose Petals Pink, Rose Petals Red

Betty Jane Schutte
Minnetonka, Minnesota

T he tugboat whistle was always the signal to run across the
high banks above the churning, dark-gray river. We didn't
think of dangers there, only of the fun we could have hiking the
path, so Donny, our teenage neighbor, a tall boy with long legs
and big feet, pulled Marilyn, my cute, pudgy younger sister in
our red metal wagon and off we went, even though we
shouldn't have gone as the river banks were not a playground
for kids.

Marilyn was only five and couldn't keep up with Donny, Lois,
plump, know-it-all sister, and nine-year-old me, B.J., short for
Betty Jane.

Mother warned us, "Just go to the upper path by the drive.
Don't go down the bank."

We all said okay. Mother didn't really want us to go at all, but
she thought Donny and eleven-year-old Lois were old enough
to watch Marilyn. Nobody had to watch me. I knew the river
banks like the back of my hand. Hadn't I taken every path down
there and swung many times on the vines out over the river? Of
course, I never told Mother that.

Lois didn't want me along, but I didn't care. She said to
Mother, "Does she have to come along?"

"Yes, she has to go. She can help you watch the wagon. Now,
don't go down the bank."

Lois walked in front next to Donny, and I brought up the rear.
Lois didn't like me to be near her, especially when someone else
was around. She wanted to hog the whole show. I guess I didn't
care that much because I was used to it, so I made believe we
were going on a tiger hunt in an African jungle. I'd jump around
a lot and hide behind bushes and trees and have fun by myself.
So off we went, across the street through a long, empty field of
tall grasses where we kids had an underground shack with a
real tin roof. We sped over the River Road to the boulevard
above the high banks of the old Boa Constrictor, the name I
called the river because a boy in my room at school had

drowned in it and people were always jumping off the bridges in it and stuff like that. Like a snake, the river swallowed people. But I loved it just the same and wished I were a tugboat captain instead of a plain old girl.

"There she goes," cried Donny when we spied the tugboat. "Look how long she is, B.J."

"Yeah," I said. "Count the barges. One, two, three, four, there's five barges. That's a load."

"All stacked with coal," said Lois.

"I can't see," and Marilyn stood up and teetered in the wagon trying to see the white tugboat and the five, flat, rusty-red barges heaped high with black coal.

"Watch out, Marilyn." Lois lunged toward Marilyn as the wagon began to roll. She grabbed it while Donny picked up Marilyn and put her on his shoulders.

"Let's go down to the rock," he said, galloping like a horse. Marilyn roared with delight as they disappeared through a clump of bushes on the bank.

Lois pulled the wagon handle, and we followed them down a narrow dirt path hidden by tall sumac bushes that led to a small, grassy plateau about ten feet down from the top of the river bank. Near the edge of the plateau facing the river and in the middle of the grassy area stood a huge boulder. The neighborhood kids met here often to make plans for riverbank expeditions, like swinging on vines, and digging white sand and stuff. We just said "The Rock" and everybody knew where to meet. We'd sit on or by it to whittle branches, draw maps, discuss plans or eat a picnic lunch. Some of the daring kids rolled dried leaves in newspapers to smoke, like cigarettes. I couldn't do that because it made me sick, and I'd give a swift kick-in-the-shins to any kids who teased me about it.

On either side of our grass circle a narrow path went north or south along the river bank about sixty or more feet above the river, then dipped down to follow the shore.

"Let's follow the path to Lake Street," suggested Donny. He's full of ideas I thought to myself, but said, "We can't do that. Mother warned us . . . "

"Oh, for heaven's sake, Betty," snipped Lois. "I think Donny's big enough to take care of us. We'll only go a short way."

Lois would do anything anybody else said but me. She was jealous of me, my mother said. Besides, I was more independent, and skinnier and active.

"Sure, I'll take care of us," said Donny and he plunked Marilyn in the wagon, grabbed the handle and the wheels rolled toward the narrow dirt path south toward Lake Street.

I didn't feel right about it. I had a strange feeling, kind of a tummy ache feeling, but I guess I was being a scaredy-cat. Scared of what Mother and Daddy would do it they found out, so I kind of hung back and pretended I was a lion hunter.

Close to the grassy flat land near the Lake Street bridge, we stopped to rest. Many huge oak trees hovered above us and the ground was covered with violets, wild strawberries, leaves, grasses and some poison ivy. A short distance down the steep bank from where we sat a limestone cliff dropped off about twenty feet to the ground below where it joined the shore by the river's edge. It was like a jungle, and I pretended lions lurked there while Donny pranced about like a clown. He bored me, so I didn't pay much attention to him, but I noticed Marilyn leave the wagon and sit next to Lois. Marilyn laughed and laughed while Donny showed off. She was the giggliest of us sisters in the family: Lois, me, Marilyn and two-year-old Sally who was too little to play much with us. She was a Mama's girl. Daddy called Marilyn "Gertie Gigglewater," she was so plump and jolly. Now she rocked back and forth with laughter. All of a sudden she rocked too deep, lost her balance and began to roll down the hill. I froze like an iceberg and couldn't move. I saw my dear little sister tumble head over heels, gathering speed at each roll.

"Marilyn," screamed Lois as she jumped up.

Donny leaped after her in giant strides, tearing his slacks on old branches, and Lois slid down the hill on her seat behind him ripping her pants to shreds, while Marilyn plunged over the cliff and rolled on.

I screamed and cried over and over, "Marilyn, Marilyn."

Tears so big and fast clouded my eyes as she rolled toward the deep river's edge. All along the shore the river sank down into a quick drop off, and the current was swift. I'd better run home and get Mother, I said to myself, and scrambled up the bank, but I could hardly see—the tears came so fast. I dug my fingers in the damp, musty-smelling dirt to hang on as my feet kept slipping on rocks and old leaves. I glanced back through my watery haze to see Marilyn roll to the river's edge. I thought she would sink in the water but a fallen tree branch stopped her. She lay very still as Lois and Donny ran up to her. Wild rose bushes scratched at my arms and legs as I reached the top of the bank, trembling and frightened as a hunted fawn. I sped across the drive, back though the empty field and home to find Mother in the backyard picking a bouquet of flowers. When she saw me she dropped the bouquet and ran toward me.

"Betty, what happened?"

She grabbed my boney shoulders and squeezed them until they hurt. I tried to pull away but she only squeezed harder.

"Tell me what happened?" she shouted, and I pulled back in surprise because Mother hardly ever hollered at anybody or anything.

"Mar-", I couldn't breathe. "Mari-", I took great gulps of air. "Sh-She fell down the bank," I blurted out and then howled louder than ever.

Mother dropped my shoulders and ran across the road. She couldn't run fast because she was a little bit plump, but it didn't matter as Donny and Lois came toward her pulling Marilyn in the wagon across the field. Marilyn lay on her back in the wagon, her knees pointed toward the sky. Donny lifted the wagon, Marilyn and all, off the curb and wheeled her over to us. She had scratches, bumps, black and blue marks and a swollen forehead. Miraculously, there were no broken arms or legs. Mother bent down and gently stroked her forehead and said, "Poor baby." Then she called her name. "Marilyn, can you hear? It's Mother."

Marilyn slowly opened her eyes. "Mama," she whimpered. She tried to sit up but fell back. She held out a small fist to Mother, who gently pried open the fingers. In her hand she held pink petals from a wild rose bush blossom she had grabbed as she fell. Some were dotted with blood drops from the thorns that had torn her hand. She closed her hand again and hugged the petals to her chest while Mother picked her up and carried her into the house and called the doctor.

Donny, Lois and I sat on the back porch steps and didn't say a word. We felt sick while we waited for punishment, knowing we'd be scolded and grounded. But that wouldn't be worse than feeling as sick as we did. Donny didn't stay long. His eyes brimmed with tears as he stood up, mumbled, "I'm sorry," and started for home. He glanced back, held the slit in his slacks and said, "I'm gonna get killed for ripping my pants," and he ran off while we sat and suffered.

Being scolded and grounded for the month of May, 1928, wasn't nearly as bad as being quarantined like we were in the following spring of 1929. Daddy barked strict instructions almost every morning for us to stay away from the River Drive and checked on our whereabouts each night. I almost felt like a prisoner, and a long, cold winter didn't help.

Marilyn had headaches now and then during the winter, but she didn't complain. She hardly ever fussed about anything. At least I never heard her, but that spring she got real sick after visiting a friend after school. Her teacher had asked her to stop by the girl's house on her way home from school to find out why the girl had been absent the last few days. Nobody was home but Marilyn's chum, so she asked her in. She lay in bed looking all red in the face, Marilyn said, and she told my sister that if she thought her face was red, she should look at her throat. It was like fire in there. Marilyn bent close and looked at the throat. Her friend drank from her water glass and offered Marilyn a drink. Marilyn drank some of her friend's water.

Not long after, we were quarantined with a scarlet fever sign on our front door. We couldn't go out of our yard and nobody could come to our house to play. We had to stay home from school. It was boring and sad. One good thing: Daddy came home early every night after work and brought presents for Marilyn to try to cheer her. She didn't seem too interested in them, I thought, especially the big, hardcover coloring book of animals. Once or twice I'd steal into the room we had always shared before her illness, against my parents's wishes so I wouldn't catch scarlet fever, and we colored pages together. But it didn't help. Her fever was high, she'd vomit a lot and her head and eyes hurt, so Mother and Daddy kept the shades drawn most of the time. They finally took her to the hospital one day in June and I was allowed in our room again, but it didn't seem the same.

A few days later Daddy and Mother came to my room, the room I had shared with Marilyn. It was lonely there without her. Daddy told me Marilyn had a tumor as large as my fist. The doctor said she had hurt her head pretty bad at one time and the scarlet fever poison had settled in the weak spot to help form a tumor on her brain. I cried and wondered about her fall because I felt like it was partly my fault that I didn't make us kids stay up above on the River Drive path. Mother didn't say a word. She only looked far, far away and cried when I asked how Marilyn was.

Daddy cleared his throat; he always did that when he was about to say something important. His voice shook as he said, "She's gone to be with the angels, Betty Jane. She . . . She . . ."

I'm not real smart, and I guess I didn't catch on. "How could she be with the angels?" I asked.

"Your dear little sister Marilyn died this morning, Betty," and Daddy cleared his throat again. "Early, at one-thirty in the morning, and we weren't there."

He unbuttoned the gray suit he always wore for special times and his fat tummy growled as he walked once around the room with short, quick steps. He stopped to stare out the bedroom window as he removed his glasses and polished them with a clean white handkerchief, while Mother cried and cried. Daddy cleared his throat, took her by the arm and led her out of the room. I wish they would have stayed because I didn't understand it at all. It just didn't sink in.

The next few days were not real either. Relatives came to the house and took over, sort of. No one paid attention to me or Lois or Sally. I felt lost and empty, and I wanted to talk to Mother, but no one would let me. Every time I went to Mother's bedroom a relative guarded the door.

"Don't bother Mother now, Betty Jane," they'd say to me. "Go to the kitchen and get a cookie," and they'd give me a shove in the direction of the kitchen.

Or they'd say, "Mother can't see you now, Betty Jane. Go outside and play with little Sally."

158

The next day Lois and I had to bathe, talcum and dress in our best dresses. We put ribbons in our hair and wore our shiny patent leather party shoes. They said we were going to the funeral parlor. With my pretty clothes on I felt more like we were going to a party. More stuff I didn't understand at all.

We drove to a strange part of Minneapolis and stopped in front of a large, brown frame house with an open porch around the front and all along one side. Trellises reaching from the porch floor to the porch roof were covered with vines of purple blossoms and dotted with Monarch and Tiger Swallowtail butterflies that dipped and fluttered around the purple blossoms. Near the front door a wooden swing swayed with the breeze, alone and empty, back and forth, back and forth. It made me feel lonely. We were slow to get out of the car and walk up a few wooden steps and pass the moving swing, which I did in a hurry, and then we continued along the side of the house to the middle of the porch where we stopped by two French doors. Canaries and yellow warblers flew in and out of the vines, and it was so quiet that I felt frightened. I wanted to hold Mother's hand, but Daddy's arm was around her shoulders and she seemed far away.

Soon a tall, baldheaded man in a black suit came out of the brown house and whispered to Mother and Daddy. He motioned toward the French doors. Daddy turned to Lois and me and said, "Come, Lois and Betty. We're going inside to see Marilyn."

See Marilyn, I thought. How can we see Marilyn when she's dead? So I just stood there unable to move.

"Come on," Lois said crossly as she grabbed my hand and pulled me through the French doors. I stumbled on the threshhold and almost fell, and thought to myself that Lois sure was crabby since Marilyn died, much more so to me than usual.

The light beige carpet in the sunny room jolted me. My feet seemed to sink an inch or more with each step on its cemetery-soil softness, and the sweet flower garden odor was like being in a bed of roses and lily-of-the-valley. Everywhere I looked flowers looked back at me and the sugary fragrance was so strong I felt dizzy.

At one end of the room, surrounded by wreathes and bouquets, stood a small, white coffin with white satin ruffles, and there, inside the coffin, as still as still could be, lay Marilyn. I could hardly believe it. She lay with her eyes closed and her hands clasped across her chest. She looked just as she did at home in her bed, sleeping, only much more quiet, still and pretty, not a hair out of place, and a white ribbon on the left side. I stared and stared and hoped she would breathe, but her chest under her blue and white party dress didn't move. I wondered if she also wore her best shoes. Suddenly, I could hardly catch my breath. I gasped, "I feel sick, Daddy. I can't breathe. Could we go home now, please?"

Without turning to look at me, he said, "In a few minutes."

I watched Mother bend over the casket and hug and kiss Marilyn over and over as she cried, and I wished she would hug and kiss me. I could hug her back. Then I felt sad and mad and turned to Daddy and said, "Please, Daddy, could we go home now? I don't feel so well."

"Pretty soon," Daddy said as he walked over to me. "First say a prayer for Marilyn."

I looked down at the beige carpet, up at the ceiling, around the room, anywhere as I hesitated until Daddy nudged me and I crept toward the casket like a sleepwalker. I fell to my knees and said the Our Father while Mother cried, and from the corner of my eye I saw Daddy lead her toward the French doors and outside. Then he came back and said to Lois, "Kiss Marilyn goodbye now." Lois marched to the small casket and gave Marilyn a short peck on the forehead. Even though she seemed prim and prissy, I admired her promptness as she turned and hurried out to the porch. She didn't cry. I never saw her cry in all my nine years. She kept everything inside herself except her anger.

"We're going home now, Betty Jane, just as soon as you kiss Marilyn goodbye," Daddy said to me.

Upset, I said, "No, I can't do that Daddy, I can't," and my tummy ached.

How could I? I didn't want to say goodbye to Marilyn. We'd shared our bedroom together ever since I could remember, and now she'd never sleep there again. I didn't move.

Daddy signed and frowned. "Come now, Betty. You love

160

your little sister, don't you? Kiss her. It's the last time you'll have the chance."

Daddy was very strict. I sometimes wondered if he loved me.

I raised my wobbly kness from the cushiony carpet and backed away from the casket. My stomach muscles tightened and I wrung my hands. How could I kiss Marilyn when she was so still and pale? How could I kiss her when she was dead? I can't, I can't, I told myself.

"We're waiting, Betty Jane," he said gruffly. (His gruffness was a way to hide his emotions, I learned later. At seventy years of age he lowered the shield one afternoon, and in his feelings of guilt and anguish he blurted, "Poor little Smoochie," the pet name he called Marilyn, "I should have gotten the brain specialist from St. Paul. Why didn't I, why didn't I?" and he cried a bit, something he seldom did, like Lois.)

As soon as we got home I said, "I think I'll go to my room and lie down."

I fell on the bed, the big double bed Marilyn and I had shared when she was well, and buried my head in the pillow, but couldn't sleep. I missed my partner; I missed her so much. Our bedroom didn't seem as bright as it used to. And the daybed she used when she was sick was gone.

A few days after the funeral I stood by "The Rock" and wondered if I should follow the path to the Lake Street Bridge. I knew I shouldn't be there, but I missed Marilyn so much I thought that if I went to the spot where she fell it might help. I felt that maybe if she hadn't fallen and hit her head she'd still be here.

Taking the south path I retraced the trail, thinking each plant, shrub and tree looked bigger and greener today and I forgot there were so many bushes, especially rose bushes. I stooped to touch the pale pink blossoms of a wild rose bush, and my stomach turned over as I wondered if this was the rose bush Marilyn had grabbed on her fall. The blossoms smelled so sweet – they smelled almost like the room at the funeral parlor. As I sniffed them a tear fell, the first tear since Marilyn died. I felt lost and very lonely. "Oh," I cried out loud, "Marilyn, I wish you were here."

I ran forward in anger and bewilderment. The path turned

downhill toward the river several yards ahead, and if I followed it I'd reach the shore of the river. I doubled back along the flat bank, stopping to stare into the dark water and the swift current that tumbled sticks, leaves, bits of paper and debris southward. I gazed down at the steep drop off of the river and shuddered—it plunged downward so quickly. Soon I reached the tree with the broken branch that had held Marilyn from the mighty, snake-like river. Its leaves touched the grass like a blanket and the branches were arranged like an alcove, a nest, a bed to rest in.

"Oh, Marilyn," I cried out again and threw myself facedown into the leaves and branches, hardly feeling the stings and scratches. I cried long, long sobs. "Marilyn, come back, come back," I blurted.

I kicked my legs and beat my fists into the ground.

When no more tears would come, I stopped crying and rolled over on my back and stared up through the tree branches. The sky seemed miles and miles away, just like Marilyn. The long grass was damp and my skinny frame ached; I sat up and ran my hands along the drooping branches of the fallen limb. I thought, what good did it do for the tree to stop Marilyn from falling in the river? She's dead now, anyway. I turned on my knees to pat the ground where she had lain and said aloud, "Marilyn, I wish you were here."

A speck of pink peeked through the long grasses. I parted the soft green grass and pricked my finger in my haste. There was a small wild rose bush. Instantly I could see the crushed rose petals in Marilyn's hand after the fall. "This is a gift to me from Marilyn," I said aloud as I looked up through the trees at the sky. "Marilyn, I just know it's from you."

I pawed ferociously at the ground with my fingernails. "I'll take you home," I said to the rose bush. "I'll put you in the best spot in the garden where I can see you everyday. Oh, dear, dear Marilyn," and I dug and dug.

My fingers weren't strong enough for the digging job, so I scurried around and found a flat chunk of limestone by the river's edge. I plunged it into the ground, tearing away the earth in soft chunks, taking big globs of black soil to cover the roots. Holding this prize in my dirt-filled hands, I darted back up the fatal path.

162

"I'll plant you as soon as we get home," I said to the small prickly rose bush. "I'll put you in the corner garden where the tulips grow each spring, the tall tulips that Daddy loves so much. You will be the only rose bush there, and I'll see you every day. The pink and red petals will remind me of Marilyn the rest of my life."

At that moment I knew Marilyn was in heaven. I could feel her near me. I hoped this feeling would come again and again all my life. I felt the best I had in a long time, so good I would even let Lois smell the blossoms of the rose bush.

Orange

Helen Earle Simcox
Mankato, Minnesota

Orange, may I warm my hands
at your fire?
You are the color of
love and
of the holy.
When I was small I sipped you
from a frosted glass
and
your warmth turned cool but
sweet in my mouth.

You glow like praise on
autumn hills;
you warm
the ancient stone of
canyon walls.
But
when night nears
you seek a far horizon,
lingering there to greet
a virgin star.

A prophet saw you blaze
within a bush
that did not burn
in Horeb's
wilderness;
apostles saw you falling as
bright tongues of
flame upon
an upper room.
You are the color of
love and
of the holy.
Orange, may I warm my heart
with your fire?

excerpt from
Out of the Depths

Annette P. Oppegard
Saint Paul, Minnesota

I t was a beautiful Friday morning in July of 1925. I was sixteen years old and was out in the backyard of our farm in southern Minnesota where I lived with my parents, two brothers and two sisters. I was enjoying the lush green lawn and the beds and rows of various flowers that blossomed in profusion under my mother's skillful hands. I didn't really want to go back into the house because we had much to do that day, and I wasn't feeling very well. Guests were coming for Sunday dinner, and the house had to be spic and span clean. There was baking to do and food to prepare. But since I knew mother needed help, I returned to the sweeping and dusting.

As the hours went by, I felt worse and worse. My head throbbed. I felt nausea and a deep exhaustion. I had no pain, but I felt as if my whole body was being drained of its ability to function. I went to my room upstairs to lie down for a while and I fell into a fitful, restless sleep that lasted through the night. By morning my body ached from head to toe, and a great heaviness seemed to press down upon me. Little did I realize then how long it would be before I'd leave that bed again.

I wanted to go to the bathroom, but I felt too ill to get up without help so I called my sister Esther. "Please help me to the bathroom" I said. "I don't think I can make it by myself." "All right," Esther said, "just put your arms up around my neck and I'll pull you up that way." "I'll try," I said. With great effort I moved over to the edge of the bed and started to reach for her neck. My right arm made it part way up but my left one lay unresponsive in the bed. Fear gripped us both as we recognized the symptoms of the polio epidemic that was sweeping the area that summer. Neither she nor I said a word, but we knew. Hadn't we just been talking yesterday about how bad we felt over the news that one of our friends had come down with the disease? But surely it couldn't happen to us! Mother came, and I saw in her eyes the same fear I felt. None of us would verbalize our

165

fears—hoping against hope that we were wrong. Fighting back her tears mother said, "I'll go and call the doctor."

Dr. Grinnell's office was in a small town ten miles from our home. He had no assistant and only one nurse. If a call came that would take him out to someone's home, he would have to take care of the patients in his office first and make house calls after office hours. Every doctor for miles around was besieged by urgent requests for home visits and they scarcely got any rest. Dr. Grinnell didn't make it to our house until Sunday.

By that time the paralysis had spread over my entire body. I couldn't move my head, my toes, or anything in between. I could barely gasp out one word at a time when I tried to talk. I seemed to hover on the verge of unconsciousness all day. As the doctor examined me, he shook his head slowly and motioned for my mother to follow him out of the room. He had known our family for many years, and he dreaded the task. How could he utter the wretched words that would bring us all face to face with the harsh facts of my illness.

Gently he put his arm around my mother's shoulders and, in a voice choked with emotion, said quietly, "She may not live through the night. And if she does, she may always be bedridden and helpless. She has polio."

Up until this moment my mother had refused to admit that such a fate could possibly befall the daughter she loved so much. Now she was being forced to face the reality she had dreaded and she broke down for the first time and sobbed. After a time she wiped her eyes and with a look of defiance exclaimed, "She is not going to die, and I am going to see that she recovers. I will not give up." She came back into my room with a smile on her face. She didn't tell me what the doctor had said until years later. No one needed to tell me what the diagnosis was. I knew, but was too sick to care.

The nearest hospital was thirty-five miles away, but my father had no insurance—very few did in those days. Dr. Grinnell admitted that neither hospitals nor doctors really knew how to treat polio patients because very little was known about the disease. Mother said she would rather take care of me herself at home if the doctor would agree to come every day. He agreed, and so began the battle.

166

For a week I hovered between life and death, only vaguely conscious of what was going on around me. I drank some liquids but ate no food. I couldn't lift a finger to do anything for myself. The crisis came on the tenth day. My mother had given me my bath, and I was exhausted. I fell into a deep sleep while the doctor stood by. Turning to her he said, "She will either die in her sleep, or she will wake up and start to recover."

The family gathered around my bed and spoke in hushed tones while keeping their eyes riveted upon my face. My breathing was shallow, and my heart was racing so fast that the doctor could not count the beats. For four long hours I lay in a deep sleep but, finally, in late afternoon I opened my eyes and looked around. I saw happy faces bending over me and heard them say, "Thank God! She'll live!" After many days of suspense and worry, the family could now go back to the daily tasks they had been neglecting so long. The crisis was over.

For my mother and me, however, the real battle was just beginning. I had been granted life, yes, but the future quality of that life was going to be determined by whatever could be done to restore my bodily functions to as nearly normal as possible. It seemed like a formidable task. If mother had any doubts about my complete recovery, she never let it show. She was always smiley and cheerful and tireless in her efforts. I noticed that her eyes were often red, but she set about with great determination to run her household and take care of me as efficiently as possible. My bed was moved into the room on the first floor which had been our parlor. There I could lie and look out the big window at the road that went by our farm, or at our beautiful yard.

A neighborhood girl who had taken nurse's training was hired to come and live with us and relieve mother a few hours each day. I could do nothing on my own; I needed constant care. The doctor still came every day and always tested my reflexes. Polio victims lose their reflexes in the limbs which are affected. None of mine responded. My left arm was the worst, and Dr. Grinnell decided to put it in a wire cast so it would have complete rest—exactly the opposite of the method which came into use later on. Continued movement is the key to keeping nerves and muscles from atrophy.

My mother stood by and watched that arm practically shrivel

167

up before she decided to take matters into her own hands. She threw the cast away and started her own brand of treatment. Day after day she used the edges of her hands to chop gently up and down my limbs to improve circulation and keep the nerves active. She propped my feet up with pillows so they wouldn't flop over and stretch the cords. She seemed to know that I'd never walk straight again if those cords weren't kept normal. She sensed my needs and spared no effort to help. The doctor wanted desperately to see some progress in my condition, but day after day went by and I was no better. One day he turned to my mother and said, "If you will permit me, I'd like to call down a specialist from the University of Minnesota to examine her. Perhaps he might know of something that might help her and give us the prognosis for her future." My mother readily agreed, and we waited eagerly for his arrival. Finally, one day when Dr. Grinnell drove into our yard we could see there was a young man with him. They came in and Dr. Grinnell introduced the specialist. He quickly began the examination while the family and I waited for some words of hope. After what seemed like an incredibly short examination, he turned to my mother and very matter-of-factly spoke the words we had hoped never to hear. "She will never walk again and will never be able even to hold up her head without a brace on her neck. Nothing can be done."

Those few short words brought my hopes and my world crashing down about me, but the young doctor just turned on his heels and walked out, seemingly unaware of the sentence of doom he had just pronouced. Dear old Dr. Grinnell looked with consternation at the young man's departing figure. Then he turned to me as I fought back the tears and said gently, "Don't listen to that young whipper-snapper, Annette. He doesn't know everything. You and I will show him a thing or two, and you will get well." Whether he really believed that or not I will never know, but his words gave me the courage that I needed very badly right then. I couldn't believe that my dream of a career as a teacher was ending before ever beginning. I was eager to learn and loved school. I felt that the more knowledge I could absorb the more I would have to pass on to my students some

168

day. I could not, and I would not, let my dream die. I would fight back with every resource at my command. I would not resign myself to being a helpless, bedridden cripple for the rest of my life.

And so began the struggle which was to last for the rest of my days. It had now been seven weeks since I had become ill, and I still could not feed myself or even sit up. My body had wasted away and every movement caused me pain. During one of the doctor's visits he turned to my mother and said, "I don't think there's any more reason for me to come any more. I can't do anything more for her." With dismay in her voice mother replied, "If you can't do any more, would you mind if I called in another doctor?" "I should say not," he replied. "If anyone else can help her, it will make me happy. I just don't know of anything more I can do."

A young osteopathic doctor had moved into town recently and mother decided to call him. Since he was eager to make a reputation for himself, he arrived at our house in short order. Mother said, "I don't know if you can do much because she hurts so we can hardly touch her." "We'll see," he replied. With skillfull yet gentle hands he worked on my limbs and along my spine, and it didn't hurt at all. I felt wonderful, and the stirrings of new life seemed to start in my body. "I'll be back tomorrow," he said as he went out the door. That night I rested better than I had at any time since I'd became ill.

In the days that followed I found I was able to do something more each day. I started feeding myself and swinging my feet at the edge of the bed. I was elated even though progress was painfully slow. As soon as I was strong enough, my father started carrying me to the car and into town for my treatments instead of having the doctor come out. Thus far I had not been able to put any weight upon my legs, but I was determined that I was going to walk to the table by Christmas. That was the goal I set for myself and each small accomplishment that brought me nearer the goal was a victory. But no matter what the doctor or I did, my left arm stayed immobile from the elbow to the shoulder, and was to stay that way for the rest of my life.

The whole family stood around me when the day came in December that I was to try taking my first step. With a person on either side, I put my feet on the floor. My legs held me up, and hesitantly I took three steps. A rousing cheer went up from those standing—I felt like the victor in a race.

Tiger's Revenge

Doris Fuller Pylkas
Inver Grove Heights, Minnesota

T he words of his father's curse were seared on Tou Yer's mind. He would always remember that shock on his father's face as he moaned, "I will never forget that you betrayed me, and I will pursue you for as long as you live. I will never lift this curse."

On many sleepless nights Tou Yer had pondered these words and decided to find a holy man wise and experienced enough to enter the land of the dead to convince his father of his innocence.

On the night he had decided to make this journey, Tou left the long bamboo house in the clearing and glanced around fearfully. He crouched low, protected by the bushes on the edge of the Laotian forest, his sparkling black eyes ever alert to danger. He slipped into the dark, silent woods with one lithe movement. Noiselessly he stood watching for the tiger, then he heard it . . . a low growl, a warning of things to come.

As he listened, he fingered the three strings on his wrist. Each one was a wish for his safety on this dangerous journey. Chou, his brother, and his sisters, Mai Lee and Bo, had encircled his wrist with strings expressing their desire for his safe return. He felt protected with their blessings to guide him.

Mai Lee, his younger sister cautioned, "Be alert, and let the good ghosts protect you. Don't stop watching for danger." Fondly he replied, "I will, especially because you wish it for me."

Thinking of her warning, he redoubled his efforts as he travelled northward up the Annamite chain near the northern border of Laos where the shaman lived on the top of the mountain.

As he walked, Tou Yer's mind turned to the day, three years ago, of his father's capture. His father, Gao Vang, had returned from Vientiane where his unit had broken up to lead his family out of Laos to the safety of Thailand. The Pathet Lao had nearly followed Gao Vang to his mountain home.

Relentlessly the Communists had sought out any soldier who had helped the Americans in the '70's and destroyed them and their families. Gao Vang was one of the Hmong mountain people who had helped the Americans. Familiar with the mountainous terrain with its protective underbrush and broad-leaved pines, he and his family were travelling by foot. Finally they were within a half a mile of the Mekong River where they would cross into Thailand and safety.

That day Tou Yer had been straining every nerve to listen for the soldiers. He jumped involuntarily when his father grabbed his arm and whispered. "I'm going ahead to see where the soldiers are. If everything is all right, we can get to Thailand tonight. If I'm not back in a half hour, tell Chou to take the family across the Mekong River as fast as he can."

When the half-hour was up, Tou Yer called to Chou and said softly, "Take your sisters and mother and get as close to the river as you can. Give me an hour to return, and if I don't come, cross the river. If there are no boats to take, swim."

Tou Yer moved cautiously and hid in the underbrush. As he moved in the direction of where he had last seen his father, he noticed broken branches. The ground was trampled by heavy boots. The sight in the clearing made him catch his breath. The Pathet Lao soldiers were beating and jeering at his father. They were shouting, "Gao, we know your son's name is Tou Yer. Where is he?"

Suddenly Tou Yer was grabbed by the scruff of the neck. He looked down at a pair of dust-covered black boots and dirty jungle fatigues. Raising his eyes he saw an evil leering face, black beard and narrowed eyes. The man's breath smelled of garlic. Shaking his victim, the soldier shouted, "Look what I found skulking in the woods." Giving Tou another shake he said, "What is you name?"

Tou Yer croaked his name. The soldier scoffed, "Now we'll find where the rest of the family is." And he dragged Tou by his arm to the clearing where his father was lying. Roaring with laughter he taunted, "Look, we have your son. He told us exactly where you were," then malevolently yelled, "He even drew us a map. Ask him . . . he won't deny it."

Sixteen-year-old Tou Yer trembled with fear. He struggled to

172

get out of the soldier's grasp. He wanted to run to his father. His captor spat on the ground in disgust. "We captured your son, and he told us everything. Now he's going to tell us where the rest of the family is."

Gao protested, "My son is no traitor, and he would never tell you where I was."

The soldier commanded, "Tell you father the truth. You turned him in for the money the captain gave you." Tou had the denial on the tip of his tongue, but fear made it freeze in his throat. Reproach showed on his father's swollen face. He willed his son to speak, but Tou Yer was too terrified.

The silence was broken by Gao Vang's last words, "I will never forget you betrayed me, and I will pursue you for as long as you live. I will never lift this curse." As Gao Vang uttered these words, he began to change, his face was transfigured into an animal-like visage, his fingernails curved and sharpened at the point. With a terrible gutteral shout—half animal, half man—he turned into a tiger. The soldiers, transfixed with surprise and horror, raised their rifles to shoot the beast. They hesitated just long enough for the tiger to leap into the forest. Shocked, Tou Yer realized he had to act. Taking advantage of the situation, he escaped too.

Engrossed in this memory Tou Year had become careless about watching for the tiger when he suddenly heard a threatening growl in the distance. Then he recalled Chou's wish. As Chou placed the second string on his wrist, his round face earnest, he'd warned, "I want you to carry a knife in your belt. Listen for the chattering of the birds and the monkeys. They will warn you if any large animals are near."

Absently Tou tightened the red, embroidered cummerbund as he noticed the warning sounds of the birds. He grasped the handle of the knife tightly. He gasped as amber, slanted eyes peered at him through the thicket. Swiftly he zig-zagged up the path to throw the animal off his scent. Not knowing where the beast was sent an involuntary chill up his back.

As he climbed, the steepness of the path and the loose stones nearly made him fall. He did not dare get careless. The pines were thinning out at this altitude, and he had less cover to protect him. When he was a child, his father had taught him to stay downwind if his life was ever threatened by an animal. When he came to a stream, he walked in it so the tiger would lose his scent. His heart pounded with fear when a monkey flew by on a low branch. He was nearly there, but at any time he could be outsmarted by the tiger.

The danger passed. He relaxed enough to anticipate the planing and cooking occurring at home for the shaman's ceremony. The preparations had to be perfect because this was such an important event in You Ter's life.

For such a rite the whole Vang clan would be present. In his mind's eye, he could see the girls wearing the White Hmong costume—their black blouses with blue collars and cuffs. The men wore pantaloons with bright embroidered belts, and he saw the pandau apron skirts of the girls with the emroidered cross-stitch designs. As the girls chopped the vegetables for the sweet soup, he could hear the tinkle of their coin necklaces. Their waist-length, blue-black hair swayed as they carried water and firewood. His mouth watered thinking of the smell of spices and the roast pig turning on the spit, a gift to those in the land of the dead as well as part of the feast.

Time passed so fast that he was surprised when he came to the holy man's hut. He tapped on the open door, and the holy man beckoned him to enter the kitchen at the end of the cottage. There was soup bubbling in the kettle suspended over the fire in the hearth. The holy man, dignified and cool, said, "What do you want?"

Gathering courage Tou explained with a bow, "I have come a great distance, almost from Vientiane, to see if you will help me with a problem of great importance." He told him the story of his father's capture and his curse.

The holy man replied cooly, "I suppose you want your curse lifted. How do I know what you tell me is true? You have no proof that you didn't betray your father." His eyes glared with suspicion.

Tou thought for a moment and replied, "I have mourned not only for his cruel death but for his belief in my betrayal. I wouldn't have gone to look for him if I had betrayed him."

The shaman snapped, hoping to catch him off guard, "How

174

much did the captain pay you?" His long gray hair fell across his wrinkled face.

Tou Yer held his head in his hands wanting so much to convince the shaman of his sincerity.

"You needed money badly. How much did they promise you?" The holy man's thin cheeks were sucked in, emphasizing his high cheekbones and accusing eyes.

Tou finally replied, "No money can pay for a wonderful father. I loved him more than anything in my life. I worked a year to get enough money to engage you."

The shaman's face relaxed, and he said, "I wanted to hear you say this. You have convinced me." Then he added, "Now let's get started." He donned his loose black clothing, packed his ceremonial needs in a box, and put out the fire. His sinewy body promised protection for anyone going with him. As they descended the now-familiar path, they occasionally heard a menacing growl . . . enough to know that the tiger was still stalking them.

Tou thought longingly of the safety of home, but the prospect of freedom from the curse was worth all the trials. He hastened his pace as he neared home. He hoped everything would be ready. He was respectful of all holy men, but this one was more awesome because he could enter the "otherworld," a power that could not be taken lightly.

When he arrived, the people of the clan were glad to see him; they obviously had been worried.

The last wish which was given by his older sister Bo was about to be fulfilled. She had said, "I hope you can find a shaman who can enter the land of the dead," and she added sadly, "And that father will forgive you, and you will be at peace."

Just then Tou and the shaman saw a group hovering around the ceremonial table. The men came over to Tou Yer and the holy man and bowed in polite obeisance. The clan leader said, "Come sire, everything is in readiness." A long bench was placed in front of the table with a dagger stuck in the ground to protect the shaman at the entrance to the "otherworld."

As final preparation Chou was chosen to cover the holy man's face with the ceremonial cloth. The shaman began to shake his tambourine-like bell. His body shook faster and faster until it quaked violently. Chou's job was to hold him tightly as he entered the land of the dead to protect the shaman against the evil one at the entrance. The red cloth covering the holy man's face was waving violently as Chou held him. Chou held him until the furious shaking subsided.

Finally, the priest chanted in a dialect of Hmong only priests and ghosts understood. The chant came to a crescendo, then died to a whisper. The shaman had instructed Tou Yer and his family to conduct themselves as if nothing had happened once he had broken through to the "otherworld." Tou longed to know if his stern father would forgive him, and if he liked his gifts of food and money.

The table was set with the Chinese candles, cups of rice, and six small cups in exact order for the shaman's use—ready for the holy man to present to Tou Yer's father. He spoke to the ghosts in the special language and presented the gifts. Tou Yer wondered if his father would enjoy the roast pork, his father's favorite food.

The ceremony completed, the shaman called Chou and Tou Yer to him saying, "Now I'll explain to you what I learned in the 'otherworld.' Your father believed you had betrayed him, but I reminded him that you too had been captured, and you were very young and afraid."

Tou Yer interrupted, "I would never betray him."

The holy man frowned his disapproval at the interruption.

"I told your father all the things you had done to clear your name. I told him how far you had gone to find me, and that I had served many sons because the soldiers had lied about them. I explained, 'You know the Pathet Lao are liars and like to watch a father's grief.' When I gave him the money and gifts, he accepted them graciously and he especially liked the roast pig."

Then the shaman instructed Tou, "Now go to the edge of the clearing. Do not be afraid; the good ghosts will protect you. Speak to your father, the tiger."

With trepidation Tou walked the hundred yards to the edge of the clearing. His body shook, and he could hardly hold his hands steady. The palms of his hands began to sweat, and he drew back in fear as he saw the outline of a tiger in the brush and heard the low growls. After several frozen moments, the tiger stepped out to meet him. For a moment, Tou was terrified. Then the tiger took a step closer and gazed at Tou with a father's deep love. Tou drank in that love and gently, tremulously touched the great head. The last wish was fulfilled; the curse was broken.

Abacus

Meg Kramer
Truman, Minnesota

If one has need of an abacus
To reckon autumn's fleeting hours,
To tally mellow days before the cold of winter
Sends birds south,
Long rows of swallows on a telephone wire
Will do as well.

Dry Bones

Ebba M. Kingstrom
Sacred Heart, Minnesota

There was a black iron fence in front with a clanging iron gate which, if pushed gently, would latch and stay closed. If pushed too hard, it would swing the other way and stand open, and then the dog would get out. But best about it was that a ten-year-old could stand and swing on it, back and forth, back and forth, the iron hinges squealing and the latch protesting as the gate passed it. Each iron rod forming the fence was anchored in concrete at the bottom and bent over at the top, u-shaped, upside down. Each double rod was intertwined with its neighbor rod, thus making a very sturdy and attractive fence.

Almost all the houses in Galveston were enclosed with iron or wood fences, or with thick shrubbery. This defined the boundaries and the children knew where they were supposed to stay. Of course, fences were fun to climb over, sit on and perhaps walk on top of—like Tom Sawyer did showing off for Becky.

Number 1610 was a tall narrow two-story white wood house, with green slatted wood shutters on the windows, and crawl space underneath between the brick foundation posts.

There was a date palm in front of 1610, and pink and white blooming oleander bushes lined the whole block. Some date palms bore fruit, but the one in front of 1610 never did, because, the children were told, there should be two. They never could figure that out.

Two ten-foot square porches graced the front, one on the lower level, the other directly above on the second floor. The children were never allowed out on the upper porch, but sometimes they sneaked out and oohed and aahed as they braved the heights and looked out over the neighborhood, scurrying back and closing the door softly if they heard Mother coming. The wood railing criss-crossed into scrollwork at the corners. The rounded wood joists with knobs on the ends under the upper porch corners looked like arms and hands holding up the porch.

The three-foot crawl space under 1610 was a great place to

have a hideaway in the summertime. Nils and his sister, Jenny, could sit upright. Mother gave them four old threadbare blankets to spread out on the sandy earth, and here prize collections were arranged in neat piles: stones sorted into large and small sizes, and sea shells from excursions along the sandy white beaches of the Gulf of Mexico—only eight blocks away. Sand dollars were prized most, and Nils and Jenny always searched for perfect ones. They only had three perfect shells in their collection.

"Jenny, remember how Papa used to walk with us to the beach and help us find shells? He used to find perfect sand dollars." Nils caressed the three perfect shells. Mother wouldn't let him go to the beach alone or with his friends since Papa had died. And the Saturday movies had dwindled to one a month. Mama said they couldn't afford it.

They could use conch shells to listen to the roar of the water, imagining stormy seas—especially the sound of the Gulf as it poured over the city in 1900. Papa had told them about that, how the hurricane had swept the water ten-feet high across the island. Nils and Jenny would shiver gloriously as they imagined the grisly details of that thirty-years-past disaster.

Nils coaxed their old dog Bucky under the house, and the pet loved to lay there in the coolness. Sometimes he would dig holes and unearth more treasures: old flattened cans, interesting shaped pieces of wood, bones, and rusty nails.

"Watch out for the rusty nails," Nils warned. Jenny nodded solemnly. They remembered when Sam, their older brother, had stepped on a rusty nail, got an infection, and hobbled around for many days with a swollen bandaged foot. Finally, the doctor came to cut and clean out the infection, and Sam screamed, it hurt so. Nils and Jenny sat on the porch, looking down at their own bare feet, vowing to wear shoes forever after that. But in three days the shoes were shucked aside, and they were barefoot again, gleefully rubbing their feet in the sandy soil, picking up pebbles with their toes.

As Nils puttered with their piles of collectibles, he thought how different things were around home since Papa died. Papa had been sick for a long time, but at least he was there to talk to. Now Mama was always finding some chore for him to do, and she was always asking, "Where are you going? What are you going to do? Who are you going with?" Even Sam and their two older sisters, Emma and Hester, were forever being questioned. Consequently, they spent as little time at home as possible, and certainly had no time for Nils.

So Nils had retreated under the house to play with Jenny, who was surprised but pleased to have him there. Mama didn't yell at him when she knew he was playing with his little sister.

Under the house it was strange how the footsteps sounded from above. Feet without any bodies. Nils and Jenny made up a game trying to guess whose feet were walking there. Nils even imagined how his father's footsteps would have sounded. Maybe like Sam's, who was sixteen, six feet tall and muscular. Only Papa was bigger with broader shoulders—a real man's man. Nils cringed a bit as he thought of his own nickname, Stringbean. Mama told him that as he got older he would fill out like Sam and Papa, but he doubted it. He could only see himself as a stringbean, even when he was twenty.

Voices drifted downward to the two children. They whispered and giggled over the scraps of conversation they heard from above—mostly Mama scolding one of the older children: "Hester, curfew is at 12:00." "No, you're too young to get married. . .have to work a while yet and save." "Emma, your friends are getting too wild." "Sam, we can't afford to buy a new car!"

Soon, Jenny, tired of footsteps and voices, went back to putting her dolls down to nap, scolding them as she tucked them in, and softly singing "Sleep, Baby Sleep."

Bucky was digging holes again, the dust flying over to the blanketed area. Nils threw a pebble and Bucky ran farther away to dig furiously, thrusting his nose into the hole now and then, measuring the progress. Nils lay on his stomach, chin propped in his hands, watching him, mostly because there was nothing else to do.

"Whatcha got, Buck?" Bucky pulled out what looked like a bone, and then commenced digging again, sniffing and nosing until his snout and eyes were plastered with sand. Nils slithered over to the dog's digging, skirting streams of flying pebbles and dirt. He retrieved the bone and added it to the pile on the blankets. Idly, he spread out the pile, sorting similar sizes together. Some were obviously soup and pork chop bones, but others were different. He tried to fit broken pieces together, like a jigsaw puzzle.

"Hey, what're you doing under there?" Nils' friend Blister was down on his knees peering around in the shady space under the house, looking for Nils. Nils hurriedly crawled over and out into the daylight, eye-spots dancing in the bright sunlight. "What're you doing under there, String? Hiding?"

"Naw," Nils replied. "Been watching Buck dig up stuff. Come on under. It's cool anyway." The two friends crawled over to where Bucky was still sending out sprays of sand and pebbles, littering the area with smashed cans, jar covers and small bottles.

"This must have been a garbage dump! Who's that over there?" Blister motioned toward a shadowy figure on the blankets.

"Oh, that's Jenny. She's playing with her dolls."

"So that's where you've been instead of playing with us guys, playing with Jenny and her dolls!"

Nils gave him a shove and Blister sprawled in the dirt, "Okay, okay. Just kidding!"

"C'mon, Blister, help me get some of this stuff over to the piles on the blankets. Bring unbroken bottles, nice stones, and bones."

"Wow, Nils, have you ever got bones! Some of them look like human." Blister's father was a doctor, and Blister loved to look at the skeletons and body parts displayed in his father's lab. "Let's see if we can lay out a skeleton."

The two boys worked diligently, exclaiming "Look at this" as they found an obvious toe or finger or piece of skull, holding it up gingerly.

Nils began to sing, "Dem bones, dem bones, dem dry bones. Oh, hear the voice of the Lord." Blister picked it up. "The hip bone connected to the thigh bone; the thigh bone connected to the leg bone; the leg bone connected to the ankle bone. Oh, hear the voice of the Lord."

Blister poked Nils with a thigh bone, then laid it next to the pelvis bone. "This pelvis isn't even broken, and most of the ribs are intact in the rib cage." He hummed a few more bars of "Dry Bones." "Wish we had some good glue, String. We could glue these parts together and have a real skeleton for Halloween fun!"

But Nils didn't reply. He was only watching now, watching Blister as he fitted the lower legs to the upper, trying to determine which was the left and right. As he watched the human skeleton taking shape, he wondered about its identity. And he wondered if Papa was only a skeleton now. Finally he spoke in a low voice, "Where do you think it came from, Blister?"

"Don't know String. Maybe it came from the cemetery in the 1900 hurricane. My dad says bodies were washed out of their caskets and floated all around. Maybe when the flood went down, the bones just settled into the ground.

Nils shivered. "You think my house is sitting over a graveyard of bones?"

"The whole city was a graveyard then."

"It's getting dark. Let's go out, Blister."

"In a minute. There! Look at that, Nils! A whole skeleton— almost. Just a piece missing here and there." Blister was singing again, "Ezekiel connected all the dry bones . . . "

Nils paled as he looked at the five-foot skeleton, stretched out, staring up with open mouth. It seemed to Nils as he gaped that it looked at him and its mouth moved.

"Pretty good job we did, I'd say. Don't you think so, String? There's not two hundred bones, like a skeleton's supposed to have, but enough to make it look real!"

Blister looked around, but Nils was gone. It was dusk now, and alone under the house in the semi-darkness, Blister decided he had better leave too. He took one last long look at the eerie-looking skeleton as he backed away, then crawled fast from under the house.

Nils sneaked out on the upper porch and saw Blister run by and down the street. He wondered if Blister had seen the skeleton move too. Sitting on the floor and peering through the railing, Nils remembered when Papa used to sit out here in the cool evenings, a shawl around his shoulders. Nils would sit on the floor beside Papa's rocker and listen to tales of Papa's boyhood in Sweden and of Nils' grandfather, Sven, who had been a sea captain.

Nils felt a hand on his shoulder, and he started at Sam's voice. "Mama called; supper's ready, Nils." As they walked downstairs to the dining room, Sam asked Nils, "Where have you been all summer?"

Nils, still a little pale, told him in a shaky voice about the under-the-house hideaway where Jenny played, Bucky's digging, and finally the moving skeleton. Sam smiled a bit and told him the mouth probably moved because the jaw was loose in the head.

When school started, Nils played on an after-school junior league baseball team. Sam, and sometimes even Mama and Jenny, would come watch and cheer him on.

It was after one of these games that Nils arrived home tired and sweaty. Bucky didn't meet him at the gate as usual, but Nils hardly noticed. He cleaned up and had a salami sandwich. Finally, he thought about it and asked his mother but she hadn't seen Bucky all day. So Nils went to scout the neighborhood while Mama and Jenny went downtown grocery shopping.

"Dumb dog," he muttered as he biked around. "He's going to get picked up by the dog catcher." Eventually Nils returned home thinking maybe Bucky was just sound asleep in his doghouse or some shady corner of the backyard. It had been a very warm October day.

Or maybe he's sleeping under the house. Nils hesitated. He hadn't been under the house or even looked under the house since summer. And he wasn't sure he wanted to now. But he had to find Bucky, so he knelt and peered around in the shadowy place, seeing him a little ways in. "There he is! Lazy dog! Sleeping here when I'm hunting all over for him."

Nils called softly, "Here, Bucky. Come here, Buck." But there was no answering wag of the tail, so Nils had to crawl under, grab Bucky's leg and shake it to waken him. Becoming alarmed at no response, Nils glanced over to where the skeleton had lain, then grabbing both Bucky's hind legs in one hand, he crawled out fast, pulling the dog behind him.

Panicky now, Nils picked up the limp form, cradling it in his arms, and ran into the house, running from room to room. "Mama! Jenny! Bucky's dead!" Upstairs he went calling and, finally, out onto the upper front porch. Ten minutes later, Sam found him there.

"Bucky's dead, Sam. Just like Papa."

"Bucky was almost thirteen years old, Nils. That's old for a dog. It's still light outside. Let's go down and bury him in a corner of the garden.

"I found him under the house. And Sam, the skeleton's gone too!"

"Come on Nils, before it gets dark." So Nils, carrying his lifeless pet, and Sam with his arm around Nils' shoulders, walked slowly downstairs and out to the backyard. There were other pets buried the little corner-of-the-yard cemetery. Tooter, the canary; Slippy, their calico cat, plus a couple of her kittens; and Clementine, Bucky's mother. Mama had planted petunias and snapdragons there, and they were blooming profusely.

Sam silently spaded a two-foot hole while Nils watched. Then Nils carefully laid Bucky on the bottom, and Sam filled in the hole. Nils patted the soft earth into a rounded mound, trying hard not to cry anymore.

"I buried the skeleton bones out here too, Nils," Sam said. "My science teacher said they must be from the 1900 storm. Others have found bones under their houses too...Mama will plant more flowers here now."

Both boys stood quietly together—one tall and muscular, the other small and thin—both remembering a bigger mound of earth in another cemetery.